DIAGNOSIS DOCUMENTATION AND CODING

The Key to Reimbursement and Capitation

DENNIS M. ADAMS

HFMA® Healthcare Financial Management Association

McGraw-Hill
New York   San Francisco   Washington, D.C.   Auckland   Bogotá
Caracas   Lisbon   London   Madrid   Mexico City   Milan
Montreal   New Delhi   San Juan   Singapore
Sydney   Tokyo   Toronto

Library of Congress Cataloging-in-Publication Data

Adams, Dennis M. (Dennis Marshall), (date)
    Diagnosis documentation and coding : the key to reimbursement and
capitation / Dennis M. Adams.
        p.   cm.
    Includes index.
    ISBN 0-7863-1000-6
    1. Physician services utilization—Forecasting.   2. Insurance.
Health—Adjustment of claims.   3. Physician services utilization—
Mathematical models.   4. Diagnosis related groups.   5. Managed care
plans (Medical care)
    R728.5.A28   1997
    368.38'2'00973—dc21   96–48064

McGraw-Hill
A Division of The **McGraw·Hill** Companies

    2 3 4 5 6 7 8 9 0 DOC/ DOC 9 0 9 8

ISBN 0-7863-1000-6

Printed and bound by R. R. Donnelley & Sons Company.

This publication is designed to provide accurate and authoritative information in regard
to the subject matter covered. It is sold with the understanding that neither the author nor
the publisher is engaged in rendering legal, accounting, or other professional service. If
legal advice or other expert assistance is required, the services of a competent professional
person should be sought.
                    —From a Declaration of Principles jointly adopted by a Committee
                    of the American Bar Association and a Committee of Publishers.

McGraw-Hill books are available at special quantity discounts to use as premiums and
sales promotions, or for use in corporate training programs. For more information, please
write to the Director of Special Sales, McGraw-Hill, 11 West 19th Street, New York, NY
10011. Or contact your local bookstore.

This book is dedicated to my kids, Brandy, Billy, and Jamie, and to my grandkids, Journey and Jordyn. Most of all, I would like to express my deep love and thanks to my best friend and wife, Charlee. Adam, welcome to the family.

PREFACE

Most Americans expect to have healthcare insurance coverage. As a physician, I held a belief for many years that most, if not all, of my patients would have some form of health insurance coverage. I ordered my office staff to arrange procedures for collecting information and processing insurance claim forms, but I didn't understand the system myself. My staff plagued me with requests from insurance carriers for extra paperwork, much of which was for additional information that I felt I had already provided. These requests seemed like excuses for delaying payment or reasons for denials, which frustrated me. When I was first in practice, I rebelled, refusing to give any more time than minimally necessary to billing. I became increasingly irritated at the sight of an expanded staff dealing exclusively with insurance paperwork.

My staff was also becoming increasingly irritated with me. They too were frustrated, caught in the middle between patients who depended on their insurance to pay their medical bills and the machinations of insurance companies that required seemingly more and more information from me to process my patients' claims. My staff was also correct in their complaints about my lack of involvement. So, with great reluctance, I began to learn the business side of healthcare.

Several things became immediately obvious to me. First, I was not only in the healthcare business, I was in the credit business. My staff made me realize that if patients couldn't pay their bills with insurance, they were probably going to pay them in small monthly payments, or not at all.

The second realization was the credit I granted is based on a patient's potential insurance benefits. A patient without benefits has no good basis for credit and likely would have no way to pay me.

Finally, the most obvious realization was that without patients who could pay their bills, I couldn't provide any services at any price. As a result of these realizations, I became an avid student of the business of medical practice and of the insurance industry.

To my surprise, I found the healthcare industry a fascinating study. I completed a masters in healthcare administration and for a time served as a university department chairman teaching classes on healthcare administration. Currently, I serve as an administrator of a small, but profitable, practice group. What I have learned about the healthcare industry and insurance has brought me to some rather specific criticisms of the current state of healthcare delivery and finance, particularly concerning techniques of data capture, accounting, and statistical analysis. The skills presented in this book will enable readers to collect accurate in-office data and to adjust for inherent inaccuracies in diagnostic-driven data collection systems. Providers must master these skills to successfully, and profitably, contract with managed and capitated care companies.

Chapter 1 presents a short history of indemnity insurance. It is essential to understand the history and evolution of insurance, complete with its failures and shortcomings, to truly understand the current situation and the special problems managed care presents to physicians.

Chapter 2 discusses the fall of the fee-for-service model and the rise of credit-based healthcare. The chapter focuses particularly on Medicare, which has become the primary area for health services research. Such research has resulted in many changes to the mechanics of healthcare insurance.

Chapter 3 proposes a structure for framing diagnoses and provides the basis for accurate data capture.

Chapter 4 reviews the basics of CPT coding. It also presents an easy way to standardize coding, which will reduce errors and ensure accurate data collection.

Chapter 5 deals with actuarial data and the common errors that exist in data currently being used to predict utilization. The chapter also offers insights into how to refute common claim denials.

Chapter 6 discusses the common performance measurements of clinical variation and outcome studies and the impact of inaccurate or unadjusted data.

Chapter 7 examines over-the-counter software that can be easily used to generate accurate in-office data.

Chapter 8 discusses the role of accurate costing.

Chapter 9 deals with practical considerations of managed care contracting and many of the common legal liabilities that accompany it.

A prime point I wish to cover in this book is that insurance companies cannot predict the burden of illness of a population or the cost associated with an illness with a high degree of certainty with the data currently being collected. The data fields used by the insurance industry have not been sufficiently expanded to properly detail diagnoses so as to make them truly meaningful to people who predict healthcare utilization rates. As insurance carriers push the responsibility of utilization prediction and control to the level of providers, physicians will have to master the concept of utilization prediction or fail in business. The primary purpose of this book is to point out those actuarial weaknesses and demonstrate how in-office data can be used to create a far superior utilization model.

ACKNOWLEDGMENTS

I greatly appreciate the help provided by the Medical Group Management Association Library Resource Center. I would also like to express my appreciation to the crew at Irwin. Their flexibility and understanding made this project easier than it might otherwise have been.

CONTENTS

1
CHAPTER

History of Insurance

TODAY'S CHALLENGE IN HEALTHCARE

Just as reality forced me to learn the business side of practicing medicine 20 years ago, reality is now giving a wake-up call to all physicians. However, this wake-up call is no longer just to learn the business of medicine, but also to learn the business of insurance. Physicians will increasingly find themselves more intimately tied to the insurance industry as the practice of medicine evolves through managed care into fully capitated care.

The insurance industry has made data management and accounting the basis of today's medical practice. A medical practice must be adept at data management and accounting to compete in the coming capitated and contracting boom.

A medical practice's mastery of capitation and contracting begins with a thorough understanding of the workings and principles of the insurance industry and the economic forces that control it.

THE HISTORY OF HEALTHCARE MARKET FORCES

Most Americans are surprised to find that the health insurance industry began only 50 years ago. Before the end of World War II a simple fee-for-service system of healthcare was in place in the United States, in which the consumer was in direct control of choosing a doctor and of the amount of money to be paid for the services. In economic terms, the consumer was in charge of the wise use of his own scarce resources; he would retain physicians' services and simply pay for them as they were incurred. This was a simple and efficient economic dynamic.

In an attempt to control the inflationary tendencies of our wartime economy, the government placed caps on wages. In reaction to these caps, business owners participated in a scheme to skirt the wage controls and so attract more skilled workers, of which there was a shortage.[1] This scheme was to provide workers with a benefit package that contained provisions to cover healthcare expenses.

Benefit packages were ruled as a legal supplementation of wages and were determined to have no intrinsic value. This was the beginning of the health insurance industry, and following this ruling insurance schemes proliferated, offering larger and more attractive packages to prospective employees. Although benefit packages were not considered wages, the effect was the same.[2] Workers were attracted to employers that offered the most attractive benefit packages.

After World War II, the public believed there was a shortage of doctors. Additional pressures on the healthcare market were an increased public demand for healthcare and a system of health insurance to pay for it. An increased supply of doctors to meet this demand was made possible by the government's granting student loans and subsidies to medical schools.

As the number of doctors increased, competition grew. To attract new patients, doctors made "easy credit" arrangements with their patients through the assignment of benefits clause of their insurance contracts.[3] Doctors had thus formed a contractual obligation to both the patient and the insurance company, and this permanently altered the fee-for-service dynamic to a more complex and less efficient credit dynamic.[4]

Insurance companies thrived. The demand for benefit packages and increased competition forced insurance companies to make benefits packages increasingly generous. At that time, however, insurance companies could still maintain profits by shifting money from those who weren't sick and consuming resources to those who were sick and using resources.

Unfortunately, these economic forces did not last long. Individuals were beginning to live longer, in part because of antibiotics and other new "wonder drugs." People were not only living longer, there was also a rapidly increasing population surge, known as the baby boom. Insurance companies now faced rapidly increasing use of contract benefits. Larger outlays of capital were required to pay for this increased utilization, resulting in smaller profits for the insurance companies.

To manage increasing utilization costs while maintaining profits, insurance companies began altering benefits and services covered under policy contracts. Since most insurance policies were still provided by the employers, illnesses that predated employment could be eliminated from coverage. Such a pre-existing condition clause eliminated costly long-term care expenses. Other items singled out for elimination were the costly procedures of new technology such as CT, MRI, and PET. Organ transplants and other new surgical procedures were also eliminated. These could be deemed as unnecessary, elective, or experimental.

But costs still continued to grow, and insurance companies found other cost containment strategies, such as those based on statistics. For example, companies based coverage on reasonability of charges according to similar charge patterns in a geographic area; they also applied length-of-stay limitations. For the most part, these strategies were successful in slowing expenditures, but not in containing costs.

THE RISE AND FALL OF THE MEDICARE PROGRAM

As workers retired and were eliminated from employer-sponsored insurance coverage, a growing demand for health insurance was felt.[5] In an attempt to reply to growing demand for healthcare coverage, President Johnson created the Great Society in the mid-1960s. The disabled, the poor, and the elderly were to have insurance coverage. This political solution to a shortage of healthcare insurance would become known as Medicare and Medicaid. Medicare and Medicaid were both federal programs. Medicare would fund care for the elderly and disabled and would be regulated and governed by large regional administrations. Medicaid was developed to be a joint program with the states to fund care for the poor, and the program was to be administrated primarily by the individual states.

Originally the idea of providing care to the elderly sounded good and feasible to many. At the time Medicare was enacted, the average life expectancy was about 70 years. Some believed most elderly wouldn't live long enough to use a great amount of healthcare resources, offering a political solution at seemingly a bargain price. The idea of Medicare was attractive to many voters; it gave them a free ride, meeting their healthcare demands and putting off the debt to be borne by future generations.

In 1965, Public Law 89-97 enacted Medicare. It began as a government-sponsored health insurance program, providing equitable access and lower cost of coverage to all American citizens over the age of 65, despite race, disability, and income. It reduced the financial burden of those who could no longer work. Medicare's purpose and goals still sound noble. Whether Medicare meets the challenge is still being debated, although most now realize the program is in serious financial trouble.

The Social Security Act of 1972 added benefits for the disabled with passage of Public Law 92-603. At the same time, Medicare costs were growing and Congress had to increase premiums and deductibles.

Medicare benefits continued to grow. In 1977, Public Law 95-210 established the Rural Health Clinics Act, which funded rural health clinics. To some on Capitol Hill, this was another example of an expanding and out-of-control program. Expenses were growing at an alarming 13–16 percent per year as a result of new technologies, poor controls on reimbursement, and expanding programs. President Carter had even considered governmental regulation of the medical industry. The main problem in controlling Medicare was no one knew how.

Controls could not be recommended because the "industry" was not understood. The government began a series of studies, experiments, and policy changes that would affect the entire insurance industry.[6]

Despite the concerns of many legislators and private citizens about the system's growth, the largest and most expensive Medicare reform yet was passed. This law was known as the Medicare Catastrophic Coverage Act of 1988. Passing as Public Law 100–360, it dramatically expanded Medicare benefits to include drugs, respite care, and some out-of-pocket expenses.[7] Economic reality was dawning, however, as the new field of healthcare research produced hard numbers to work with. Such research resulted in the repeal of the Medicare Catastrophic Coverage Act of 1988 in the next year.

HEALTHCARE REFORM

With the end of the Cold War, Americans seemed ready to tackle domestic problems. Rising healthcare costs was a major part of that concern. Political polls indicated President Bush was outstandingly popular for his successful management of the Gulf War. However, concerns about his preoccupation with foreign policy and lack of attention to the home economy weakened Bush's re-election hopes.[8] As a result, the stage was set for the politicization of healthcare.

Historically, healthcare issues have been a political concern for every president since Truman. In 1988, they became even more important as Jesse Jackson ran for the presidency. In a book entitled *The Politics of Health Policy*, Vicente Navarro, who later became the healthcare advisor for Jesse Jackson, described how the return of the healthcare issue became an important political plank in the 1988 Democratic platform for the purpose of electing a president.

Navarro's participation in the formation of the Democratic platform indicated that the party had expert knowledge of the medical and insurance industry and medical economics. Armed with this expert information, the Democratic Party constructed a platform that included a call for national healthcare insurance reform. The economic and utilization patterns of consumer preferences and scarce resources, supply and demand concepts, and consumer behavior in response to the costs of providing medical services were well known to experts at this time because of healthcare research. Given these facts, it is generous to suggest that the proposal of a national healthcare reform was idealistic, and it is sarcastic to suggest that manipulative strategies were used to boost the popular appeal of a presidential candidate; however, both statements together aptly describe the proposal. A major problem with the idea of national healthcare reform was that no viable healthcare coverage model existed.

The adoption of the healthcare issue as a major plank in the Democratic platform helped usher Bill Clinton to the presidency. Clinton needed to appear serious about healthcare reform. He appointed his wife Hillary to spearhead an insurance reform plan. Hillary Clinton, together with Ira Magaziner, met secretly with unknown "contributors" to draft a national insurance plan.

Hillary Clinton and her committee traveled across the country holding meetings, ostensibly to gain information and input for the Clinton's national insurance proposal. One such meeting was held at Palmer University in Davenport, Iowa, where I was a department chairman. At that time, I taught classes in insurance, jurisprudence, and principles of practice to chiropractic students. I remember being denied access to the meeting because the list of attendees was preselected. I still wonder who picked the attendees and how the information the committee was searching for was supposed to be presented. With increasing skepticism, I watched the town meetings held by President Clinton as uninsured and needy people were paraded out to drive home the point of the healthcare crisis, all to gain support of the Insurance Reform Act.

Finally, after much hoopla, the Clintons' Health Security Plan was released. I read it with curiosity and interest. The reforms laid out a complex system of governmental boards, agencies, alliances, and other quasi-governmental institutions. The Veterans Administration, Medicare, Medicaid, and the Federal Employees Health Plan would all be abolished, rolling them into the new plan.[9] The Health Security Plan would leave in place automobile insurance and worker's compensation, avoiding two large insurance systems. No collateral, or cross coverage benefits would exists. Those who had auto or worker's compensation coverage would have to pay back the health insurance plan for any expenditures. This reimbursement would avoid costly medicolegal issues of liability and long-term disability.

The healthcare industry is large. It constitutes about 14 percent of the gross national product. Many shortcomings exist in the current healthcare delivery system, with lack of coverage issues and rapidly rising costs leading the long list of complaints. Clinton's proposal was a single, new, untried system that would replace a myriad of policies, coverages, and companies.

Congress recoiled to President Clinton's suggested healthcare reform. The main objections were that it would be impossible to implement and that the current system shouldn't be eliminated overnight and replaced with an unknown. Congress favored reform to total replacement. It became apparent that modification of the current system would be the most likely course of action.

The main problem with a national healthcare reform proposal is that no competent plan or replacement model existed. What the American people received in return for their votes was a program that reflected their wants but contained little detail as to how it could realistically meet those demands.[10]

MEDICARE AND THE EMERGENCE OF HEALTH SERVICES RESEARCH

The problem arising from high Medicare costs has had some positive effects for healthcare professionals. It resulted in a new discipline called *health services research.* Health services research has produced studies about the nature and behavior of the medical industry. Health services research produced reimbursement reform, such as prospective payments, DRGs, and healthcare delivery models as HMOs. The resulting hard numbers from this research rapidly became the basis for healthcare decisions such as the repeal of the Medicare Catastrophic Coverage Act of 1988. As a result of continued healthcare research, Medicare became the most studied and probably the best understood healthcare delivery system in America.

A prime area of study was probably due to Medicare's history of having a "retrospective payment system" that it had maintained for nearly 25 years. The retrospective payment system amounted to a system of "mail me a bill and I'll pay it, no questions asked." Unchallenged or minimally challenged medical charges opened the door for opportunistic billing practices on the part of hospitals and physicians. This resulted in a dramatic rise in medical costs, from 1.6 billion in 1965 to 6.3 billion in 1975.[11] These rising costs were so alarming that in the last four months of his term (1977), President Carter moved to control hospital costs with a comprehensive hospital cost containment program using principles derived from the Economic Stabilization Program of 1971, which was a less than effective program initiated by Congress to control inflation, including hospital costs.

The medical industry, fearing increased governmental regulation, petitioned Congress to defeat the move to control the medical industry and succeeded. In 1977 a voluntary compliance was attempted to self-regulate costs. It was called Voluntary Effort (VE) and was an attempt to avoid the threat of governmental control of the medical profession. It had broad support from the American Hospital Association, many Blue Cross and Blue Shield associations, and the American Medical Association (AMA). Voluntary Effort successfully limited growth of costs to 12.8 percent in 1978 as compared to the 15.6 percent in 1977. VE's success continued until a strong inflationary cycle in the early 1980s destroyed the effort.[12]

As a result of VE and governmental regulation of Medicare, those doing health services research divided into two camps of belief as how to control hospital costs. One camp wanted to make extensive use of the market; the other saw federal and state regulations as the key to controlling costs. These camps divide rather neatly along political party lines. Democrats favor federal and state regulation, whereas Republicans favor market forces. These preferences were apparent as conflict between the various factions in Congress arose when the Clintons attempted to pass healthcare reform some 15 years later.

THE EMERGENCE OF PERFORMANCE MEASUREMENTS AND DATA-BASED CONTROLS

Which system of control is superior is still debatable, but the effect of health services research on the healthcare system is clear. During the late 1970s and continuing into the 1980s, both camps were creating tools for measurement and evaluation of performance. Each was using the measurement tools developed by health services research to prove its point. One of the more popular tools was the development of diagnostic related groups (DRGs). In the DRG system, diagnoses are placed in related groups. Reimbursement is based on similar costs for all diagnoses in that diagnostic group. Early in the 1980s, hospital administrators were using diagnostic related groups to evaluate performance, adjusting for variance in cases, or "case mix."[13]

DRGs became an important measurement tool. The Health Care Financing Administration (HCFA), which is the U.S. government's financing branch for Medicare, used DRGs as a prospective payment system to replace the retrospective payment system that had been in place. DRGs also allowed projections to be generated.

In addition, other tools were being used to limit rising costs. In 1982, Congress attempted to control Medicare costs by passage of the Tax Equality and Fiscal Responsibility Act (TEFRA). Hospital payments were to be annually reviewed by Congress and a target rate projected. Those hospitals below that target received an incentive; those above were penalized.

The new measurement tools and techniques developed by health services research resulted in decisions based on data. The repeal of the Medicare Catastrophic Coverage Act of 1988, the adoption of a retrospective payment system, and alternative delivery methods such as HMOs are all the result that stemmed from studying Medicare.

These new measurement tools were not perfect. Criticism of

the uses and accuracy of the predicting tools came from within and without the agency. Primary concerns were about the accuracy of both the assumptions and of the data received. The failure of the DRG system to take into account the severity of illness and its impact on the cost of care is a major problem. This statistical shortcoming is a primary issue of this book.

Data gathering has become an obsession with the government and the insurance industry. Unfortunately, competition in the insurance industry and the search for the perfect statistic have compounded the problem by adding to the cost of producing care. Today, the average private care physician can employ as many, if not more, personnel to process paperwork than is required in back office staff. It has been my experience as a consultant that the average total cost for nonmedical expenditures in the average office runs greater than 60–70 percent of total costs.[14]

Although the data capture process has led to much additional work, the research has yielded valuable information and produced tremendous change in the administration of the healthcare industry.

Studies of different systems and knowledge of medical economic concepts have provided a basis for analysis and comparisons. Coding systems, even with their faults, have provided statistics that allow development of models for accurate predictions for certain applications.[15]

As dependency on health services research increased, demand for more accurate data also increased. More accurate data was needed to calculate more accurate statistics about performance and costs.[16] Medicare data was obtainable through public records, which is why Medicare became a prime field of healthcare research as opposed to the private insurance industry.

Private insurance companies are in competition with other companies so they gather data through their own methods and are unwilling to share information with competitors. This limits the insurance carrier data and the accuracy of the conclusions reached by that data.

All insurance information is gathered on the standard HCFA 1500 and UB82 forms. Even though the data fields were standardized on these forms, insurance companies requested that providers place data in specific ways to identify variation and success of individual policies. Thus, in one instance forms were to be filled out with a certain number in box X and the next time in box Y. This type of data capture delayed claims processing and added confusion to the claims process, but it enabled insurance companies to track the costs associated with specific policies. Problems such as this created the paperwork crisis now present in most offices.[17]

THE EMERGENCE OF MANAGED CARE

The debate of whether the use of the free market or of governmental control is better continues today, although the free market advocates appear to be winning at the present time. Those advocating governmental regulation propose controlling costs with more regulations on Medicare, Medicaid, and the other government-sponsored health insurance products. Free market advocates have placed hope in a reform tool developed by health services research called *managed care.*

Managed care is a reform tool used in a controlled environment. Insurance benefits are specified as to physician choice, access, specialty referrals, and use of costly technology resources. It became apparent that controlling choices controlled costs. These systems of healthcare provision are called healthcare maintenance organizations, or HMOs. HMOs gained favor with insurance companies during the economic recession of 1981–83, as private insurance companies began taking a more proactive stance on reimbursement. Initially, however, the insurance companies didn't have enough clout to control hospital behavior and thus couldn't capitalize on the savings.

Currently, Medicare is attempting to use this approach to control costs. Although the Medicare managed care product lines are small and experimental, many in Congress and the HCFA have hope for the success of the new line of healthcare.

THE NEED FOR IN-OFFICE DATA COLLECTION

Currently, dissatisfaction about the current healthcare delivery system is seemingly at an all-time high. President Clinton ran for office with healthcare reform as a major plank of his platform.[18] Dissatisfaction brought with it questions concerning such issues as cost, access, quality, coverage, preexistent conditions, fairness, management malfeasance, choice, universal coverage, and comprehensive benefits. Despite the failure of Clinton's healthcare reform plan, enough election-year attention was brought to bear on a dysfunctional insurance system as to force change.

The question is, What line of force will have to be followed in arriving at change? In my opinion, the answer is clear: the healthcare system will have to obey economic rules.

The current healthcare crisis is more about finances than healthcare. The consumer wants access to high-quality healthcare at low prices. This desire is true about every product on the market, whether it be a car, food, clothing, or anything else that can be bought.

In a cash system, economic market forces are clear and simple. The consideration and product are well defined, and the consumer purchases to a level that he or she determines. The current indemnity system of delivery and finance has been in existence for about 50 years. Rather than a cash system, it has credit as its basis. The credit basis of healthcare insurance removes control from the consumer and transfers it to the party that actually pays for the service. In a procedure-driven indemnity insurance system, like we have had for the past 50 years, the insurance carrier is in the position of trying to regulate the demand and the supply of services; and neither the supplier nor the consumer have any interest in having restrictions placed on them or their actions.

The lessons learned from healthcare research have been copied into the insurance industry. Chief among these reform tools was managed care, implemented through HMOs that control the healthcare environment of referral and utilization. The insurance industry also uses statistical measurements that limit fees and length of stay to usual and customary. Fee limitations and length of stay have become the guidelines for managed care treatment profiles.

Failure of political reform efforts and the apparent victory of free market principles indicate that the medical industry will be involved in some form of managed care for the foreseeable future. Managed care uses statistics as the basis for treatment. As physicians are forced into accepting pools of patients for treatment under managed care or capitation contracts, determining the accurate statistical basis of individual practices and comparison to the contract population become extremely important. Statistics gathered by insurance companies and offered as representative of the contract population contain data that is inaccurate because the diagnostic codes have not been adjusted for severity, complicating factors, and co-morbidities. These factors of severity, complicating factors, and co-morbidities must be adjusted for to contract intelligently in the future, otherwise the basis for managed care and capitation prediction will contain erroneous data and cause failure for many medical offices that accept this information without question.

Decisions must be made with a reasonable basis. Those needing lengthy care must be identified early. In a capitated environment, failure to identify these individuals will lead to financial failure for the contracting physician or facility. Paul Feldstein clearly stated the future of healthcare:

> Given the scarcity in the availability of resources for providing medical services, what criteria should society use for making the basic medical care decisions? A medical system that values economic efficiency in consumption and production will base its choice of the amount to spend on medical services on the criteria of satisfying consumer preferences; it will base its method of providing services on the criteria of least cost; and it will base its choice of the amount and method of medical services redistribution on the criteria of customer preference. Under this value system, medical service benefits are defined by consumer preference rather than by government or health policy perception of consumer preference.
>
> If decision makers reject the foregoing criteria, new criteria must be specified. The criterion of efficiency in production is more likely to be acceptable than is the criterion of satisfying consumer preferences. In the latter case, the alternative that proponents are likely to substitute is a "needs" approach to the allocation of medical services. Under a "needs" approach, the value placed on medical services and the resources necessary to satisfy those needs are centrally determined. Because resources are insufficient to satisfy all medical needs, an additional decision rule must be developed that will enable the decision makers to choose which needs and which population groups will be given highest priority.[19]

In a capitated environment, the physician will be given the burden of controlling utilization without a statistical basis for decision making. The physician who contracts for a capitated population is in financial peril. The prime purpose of this book is to demonstrate a simple in-office technique of how to structure a diagnostic statement for consistent data capture to quantify variation produced by disease severity, complicating factors, or co-morbidities. This in-office data collection system provides a basis of burden of illness that can be compared to the other data presented by the insurance carrier prior to contracting. In the next chapter, I will discuss the basis and basics of contracting.

REFERENCES

1. Eli Ginzberg, *Health Services Research and Health Policy, Health Services Research, Key to Health Policy* (Cambridge, MA: Harvard University Press, 1991).
2. Karen D. Davis, Gerard A. Anderson, Diane R. Rowland, and Earl S. Steinberg, *Health Care Cost Containment* (Baltimore, MD: Johns Hopkins University Press, 1990).
3. We, *Health Manpower Forecasting: The Case of Physician Supply,* (Cambridge, MA: Harvard University Press, 1991); and D. Adams, *Insurance/Jurisprudence, A Study Manual* (Davenport, IA: Brady Hill Printers, 1990).
4. Ibid.
5. Diane Rowland, *Financing Healthcare for Elderly Americans* (Cambridge, MA: Harvard University Press, 1991).
6. Ibid.; and Stewart Altman and Ellen Ostby, *Paying for Hospital Care: The Impact on Federal Policy* (Cambridge, MA: Harvard University Press, 1991).
7. Vicente Navarro, *The Politics of Health Policy, The U.S. Reforms 1980–1994* (Cambridge, MA: Blackwell, 1994).
8. Ibid.
9. The White House Domestic Policy Council, *The Clinton Blueprint, The President's Health Security Plan* (New York: Times Books, 1993).
10. Navarro, *Politics of Health Policy.*
11. Rowland, *Financing Healthcare for Elderly Americans.*
12. Paul, Feldstein, *Health Care Economics,* 4th ed. (Albany, NY: Delmar Publishers, 1993).
13. Rowland, *Financing Healthcare.*
14. Adams, *Insurance/Jurisprudence.*
15. Lawrence Brown, *Knowledge and Power: Health Services Research as a Political Resource, Health Services Research, Key to Health Policy* (Cambridge, MA: Harvard University Press, 1991).

16. Ibid.
17. Ibid.
18. Ibid.
19. Feldstein, *Health Care Economics.*

2 CHAPTER

The Fall of the Fee-for-Service Model and the Rise of the Credit-Based Physician

A surprising truth about healthcare is that physicians have been with their patients since they first started to practice. The difference is that in managed or capitated care contracting, the economic, legal, and operational dynamics are more complex, have a tendency to become confused, and offer a potential source of even greater liability.

As I stated in Chapter 1, the healthcare industry has undergone a change from a fee-for-service system to one based on credit. This change complicates the economic dynamics, offering several unique problems to the doctor-patient contract.

RIGHTS AND OBLIGATIONS IN FEE-FOR-SERVICE SYSTEM

In the past, the doctor-patient contract in the fee-for-service system was a rather straightforward arrangement of rights and obligations on the parts of both the patient and the physician. Under the fee-for-service system, a patient presents a problem, for example, a broken leg, and the physician makes an offer for a defined treatment. Presumably, the patient authorizes the physician to treat this broken leg and promises a return consideration, usually a well-defined amount of money. Assuming the duty of the physician is sufficient, or of acceptable quality, and the patient pays for the treatment, the contract is complete. In most instances, this simple doctor-patient contract has rather well-defined rights and duties for each party.

Another property of the simple fee-for-service doctor-patient relationship is a high degree of control over the contract. Each party can cancel the contract if all considerations have been fulfilled; they can then recontract with each other, with new promises and considerations, or each can form new contracts with different parties.

Primary issues in contracting from a physician's point of view consist mostly of questions of capacity and quality. Capacity concerns whether the physician can capably perform the services; malpractice issues are associated with this aspect. Quality relates to performance expectations and standards of care. The physician may begin treatment and find that the condition exceeds his or her original appraisal; or patient management may become unexpectedly complex for unforeseen reasons, causing the physician to transfer care to another physician whose care for the condition is

FIGURE 2–1

Evolution of Healthcare Finance

System	Financial Basis	Amount of Contract Control
Barter	Equitable trade	High
Gold	Common value—cash (fees-for-service)	High
Paper	Credit (indemnity-based insurance)	Moderate to low
Sand	Debit (contracted, discounted)	Low

more appropriate. In this situation, the original physician could alter or cancel the contract with the agreement and acceptance of the patient; the new parties must then form and accept a new contract.

Primary contract issues from a patient's point of view consist of questions of acceptance of the quality of the care and the price of the services rendered. The patient can terminate the contract at any given moment without reason; however, he or she is obligated to satisfy the physician for any services rendered at the time.

Of course, this is a much simplified view of the doctor-patient relationship, as other medicolegal principles of malpractice and jurisprudence apply; but rights and duties are the essence of the doctor-patient contract in the fee-for-service relationship, like in all contracting.

Figure 2–1 shows how the financial basis and degree of contract control have changed throughout the evolution of healthcare systems. These different systems will be examined more closely throughout this chapter.

RIGHTS AND OBLIGATIONS IN CREDIT-BASED SYSTEM

With the introduction of the credit-based system into the doctor-patient relationship, the rights, duties, and operational dynamics are more complex and confused. The main reason for this is the insurance carrier has interposed itself into the relationship in an attempt to control utilization. (For the purposes of this book, utiliza-

FIGURE 2-2

Operational Dynamics of Supply and Demand Cycle in Barter and Gold Systems

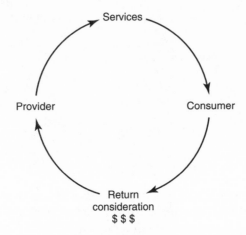

tion is defined as a combination or function of fees for services rendered and the average length of stay for the condition being treated.) An insurance company's primary purpose is to derive profits. To achieve that it must collect more in premiums than it pays in fees. Fees are a function of utilization. The more services used, the more fees the insurance company must pay out (see Figure 2–2).

In the credit-based dynamic, the physician enters into the traditional doctor-patient relationship and extends credit to the patient in the form of potential insurance benefits. The patient has a contractual obligation to the insurance company, and the insurance company has a contractual obligation to the patient. The provider, or the physician, has no rights or obligations under this contract to the insurance company. The insurance company has no obligation to the doctor, because the doctor is not a party to the contract (see Figure 2–3).

ADVANTAGE TO INSURANCE CARRIERS

Insurance carriers have formed contracts with patients promising to cover certain expenses for covered illnesses. The typical wording reads something like this: "This policy will cover medically necessary and reasonable expenses to cure and or relieve you from the ef-

FIGURE 2–3

Legal Dynamics of the Paper System

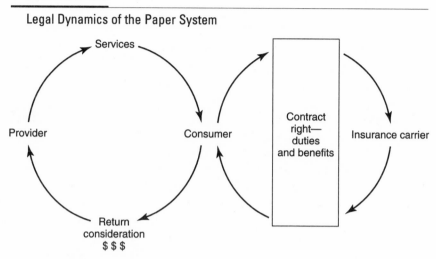

fects of accident and illness for the covered period." This wording is an attempt to place boundaries on the duties of the insurance carrier in regard to the patient's contractual rights and benefits. The difficulty in such a statement of the credit arrangement lies in the phrases, "reasonable expenses" and "medically necessary," which are vague, poorly defined, and open to interpretation.

The insurance carrier requires information from the doctor in order to determine the amount of liability and expense it has with the patient. This information is standardized on the HCFA 1500 and UB82 insurance claim forms. These claim forms are proof of loss and a demand for payment from the patient to the insurance company. The insurance company reviews the information and determines the amount of "medically necessary" charges and the "reasonability" of charges it deems appropriate to satisfy its duty to the patient.

Reasonability of Charges

The insurance company regulates the amount of moneys it pays the physician for services based upon its determination for what is reasonable. Since reasonability is subject to interpretation, insurance companies for many years have held the advantage. Insurance companies have traditionally cited statistics that show fees to be excessive compared to those for similar services in the particular geographic region. Often, however, examination of these geographic regions have shown them to include areas not comparable in costs. For example, I found an insurance carrier to have defined my geographic area of fee comparison to extend from Mexico to Santa Barbara and from the Pacific Ocean to Nevada. My Orange County, California, fees were being compared to fees in the Mojave Desert.

Recently, insurance carriers have claimed to have purchased more accurate and more definitive computer studies that compare fees within zip codes. However, this presents two problems. First, an individual physician cannot obtain the study from the carrier since it is proprietary; as such, the insurance carrier expects the physician to accept its word about the accuracy of the study. Second, recent computer programs include data on managed care and worker's compensation fees, which are not part of the usual and customary fees. It is easy to see that the insurance companies using this type of computer system are not dealing fairly with the public or the provider.

Anyone who has studied statistics can recognize that data can be manipulated to an advantage. Insurance companies use their position of insulation behind the patient to, in effect, control medical utilization; thus, utilization rates are based on statistics that have not been subject to strong scrutiny. This in-effect relationship among the insurance company, the patient, and the provider is illustrated in Figure 2–4.

Medically Necessary

The insurance company in the credit-based system has involved itself with the physician in a medical sense by determining the medical necessity of care. The insurance company, then, makes a medical decision as to the appropriateness of care. This is often based on the projected statistical performance of similar conditions with the same or similar diagnosis and an assortment of practice guidelines, which are not made known to the patient or the provider.

This is traditionally a point of contention between the patient and the insurance carrier. As a result, the insurance carrier must request additional information from the physician to justify any additional treatment. Physicians can appeal insurance company decisions on individual cases, but the procedure is time consuming

FIGURE 2-4

The In-Effect Operational Dynamics of Supply and Demand Cycle in the Paper System

The insurance carrier attempts to control utilization.

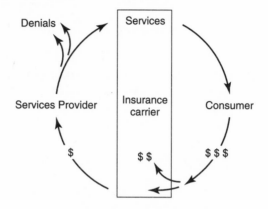

and frequently ineffective. Many of these appeals are often ineffective because the insurance carrier has a vested monetary interest in denying the care. Also, the insurance carrier is the final arbitrator of the dispute. The patient is often left feeling that he or she has received less benefit than contracted for.

In the fee-for-service, or gold, system, the patient has a strong sense of control over the doctor-patient contract. This is not so in credit-based, or paper, systems of indemnity insurance, managed care, and capitated contracting; in such systems, the patient is often left with the impression that he or she is paying well-defined amounts of money for ill-defined benefits.

I have often asked insurance companies for the statistical methodologies they use to determine an appropriate length of care for the diagnosis given. I've never received it, and insurance companies are not legally required to provide such information to providers. The insurance company's contractual obligation is with the patient. All of the rights provided under contract law are between the insurance carrier and the patient. If I wish to obtain this information, the patient must demand it from the insurance carrier. Under contract law, patients are entitled to it.

I have found most patients to be poorly informed of their insurance benefits and rights and often less than concerned with payment to the provider once the treatment has been received.

Most patients find it easier to adopt the opinion that the physicians are required to accept what the insurance companies decide to pay, so they leave the physicians and the insurance companies to fight it out.

RIGHTS AND OBLIGATIONS IN MANAGED CARE CONTRACTING

By placing itself in the role of collecting money from the patient and limiting care based on its statistical studies, the insurance carrier attempts to control utilization and thus derives profit by collecting more in premiums than utilization costs. This has permanently altered the doctor-patient dynamic.

However, with managed care contracting, the dynamic between the provider, the patient, and the insurance carrier changed again. In a managed care, or sand system, the insurance carrier is in the position of a third-party beneficiary; that is, it has an interest in the outcome of the interaction. The rights and obligations once again become more complex.

FIGURE 2–5

Operational Dynamics of Supply and Demand Cycle in the Sand System
The provider attempts to control utilization.

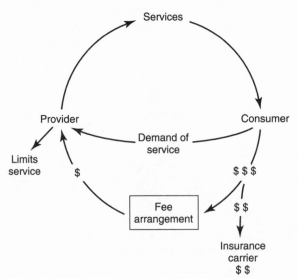

FIGURE 2-6

Legal Dynamics of the Sand System

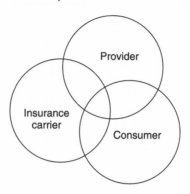

The provider has an obligation to the insurance carrier and to the patient. The patient has an obligation to the physician and the insurance carrier. And the insurance carrier has an obligation to the patient and the provider.

The contract between the provider and the insurance carrier can establish several things. Often, such a contract calls for the carrier to pay the provider discounted fees in promise of increased patient volume. In this type of contract, the carrier can directly control utilization to derive profit. Frequently, this involves control of the designated physician. The designated physician is the one who the patient must see first to start a treatment plan. Known as a *gatekeeper*, this person controls referrals to other physicians and facilities. However, this gatekeeper arrangement has created some contractual difficulties for all concerned because of the conflict of interests (operational dynamics) between the insurance carrier, the physicians, and the patients (see Figures 2–5 and 2–6).

UTILIZATION DATA

The insurance industry's attempt to control utilization has not been very successful. Although insurance companies have affected utilization, they have not controlled it. Health services research has provided more information concerning utilization profiles, and some disturbing facts have come to surface. A prime problem in establishing utilization profiles is that the data needed to predict accurate patterns does not exist. This is because utilization, as measured by fees for services rendered and average length of stay, is highly variable even when comparing similar diagnoses.

In the current system, the diagnosis—which is the driver for measuring or identifying a disease—is translated into a numeric code, called an ICD (International Classification of Disease) code, for easy computer entry. However, this code cannot account for the variations in severity of the diseases themselves. For example, given the diagnosis of chest pain, how long should the provider be given to treat it? Or how long does it take to fix back pain caused by a strain or sprain? Obviously, there is not enough information to make an accurate guess.

Insurance companies write policies to cover these diseases. But the utilization data, collected on claim forms, on which they base coverages vary tremendously. As such, every policy written has eventually failed to meet the goals of the insured and to maintain profits, because the data collected is not useful in making predictions.

Because of this inability to predict utilization accurately, insurance companies had to maintain profits, meet expenses, and pay benefits, by shifting moneys internally. But as utilization rates climbed and medical costs increased, insurance companies found it necessary to adopt alternative strategies to maintain profitability. In the past, these strategies have included altering and denying coverage, excluding certain conditions and individuals, specifying benefits, limiting charges, increasing copayments and deductibles, and selecting low-risk populations to ensure lower utilization and to control costs.

WILL MANAGED CARE WORK?

As managed care begins to take root, we are left to wonder if the phenomenon will meet the expectations and needs of the insured, or if it will fail along with all the other methods of insuring Americans. By failure I do not wish to imply that the insurance companies have not made tremendous profits. What I mean is that coverage policies have failed to maintain profitability and ultimately needed to be amended.

Before you think I'm completely biased in my criticism of the insurance industry, I would like to point out that I don't deny that insurance companies have provided to some consumers health benefits they might not have been able to otherwise afford. I also admit that physicians, as well as patients, have a part in policy failures.

Some physicians fail to collect copayments and deductibles. This artificially lowers natural economic barriers to utilization. Some physicians fail to grant credit (in the form of potential insurance benefits) intelligently as any other normal business would do with a customer seeking credit for the purchase of goods. This can allow consumers to be less than fully responsible. Providers can also play games with coding and extended care to cover the hit they take when insurance companies play their games of claim denial and payment avoidance.

The cost of utilization also rises as the public demands more and more expensive technology, even when it provides no change in treatment protocols or no additional diagnostic information. In addition, the threat of potential malpractice suits can force providers to attempt to meet the public's unreasonable expectations. This pressure, combined with the lure of additional profit gained from performing expensive tests, often forces providers to increase utilization, thus increasing costs.

In an attempt to control utilization, the insurance industry diversified upstream by forming HMO, PPO, or other controlled medical environments. In this way, the industry controls the providers in order to control costs and utilization. However, this strategy has two major weaknesses. First, to make it truly effective, the industry must educate the public about personal responsibility and the limitations of healthcare. The public must accept a wellness model, meaning that they must learn to maintain their health rather than only seek help when sick. Studies have shown this to be a slow process that yields poor results. Additionally, the behavioral changes needed in a population for this paradigm to be accepted typically take several years to develop. The average individual will change insurance carriers about every two years, thus insurance companies have little motivation to pursue such a program.

The second weakness in the insurance industry's strategy to control utilization lies in provider and patient resistance. Many doctors resent the loss of autonomy and control, and many patients have difficulty controlling the taste for expensive technology.

VARIATION IN DIAGNOSES

Even if the difficulties discussed above could be overcome—that is, if all involved were reasonable in their consumption and used technology efficiently—this system would still fail because of the inaccuracies in predicting utilization. The reason is that a statistical conclusion generated about a population is only as accurate as the data on which it is based. And the data received by insurance companies from doctors do not provide the detailed information necessary for an accurate loss (utilization) prediction. The root of this problem is that utilization is driven by procedures, reported on claim forms, which in turn are justified and driven by diagnoses that do not contain information concerning severity, complicating factors, and co-morbidities. As a result, the utilization factor of length of stay (LOS) cannot accurately reflect the time required for treatment of an individual, unique case.

Currently, the entire claim, reimbursement, and utilization prediction process centers on the diagnosis. The diagnosis justifies all treatment and procedures. Procedures are the cost drivers. The more procedures rendered, the more profit for suppliers, and the greater expense for insurance companies. A more ominous or complex diagnosis justifies more cost drivers. As a result, the diagnosis is the key to reimbursement in an indemnity market, as well as managed care and capitated markets.

From current data, we are able to construct mathematical models that accurately represent a population's disease incidence. The problem is that common mathematical models for disease incidence are the same models used for LOS and utilization predictions. Actuarial studies can accurately predict incidence of disease, that is, how often the disease occurs in a population; but they cannot predict the severity of illness. Thus, the predicted utilization costs are unadjusted for complicating factors, severity of illness, and co-morbidities.

Economics principles state that over time the profit margins of a company naturally shrink. As competition in the insurance industry grows, the margins on which those companies operate shrink. This natural decrease in profit margins creates a greater demand on the accuracy of actuarial data. As the demand for accurate data increases, the more variances in the data sample will impact predictions. Since it does not reflect the variations caused by disease severity, complicating factors, or co-morbid processes, the data presently collected will not allow for accurate utilization predictions.

It is therefore of paramount importance to have accurate data prior to capitation contracting, otherwise the physician will suffer the same fate as the insurance companies, which is failure in utilization prediction and financial loss.

3

Diagnostic Structuring and Data Collection

All insurance companies depend on the data transmitted to them by the providers to determine their present liability and potential future financial obligations under the duties portion of their issued contracts. As such, errors in the information relayed to the insurance carriers have a serious effect on present costs and predicted utilization. The principal data needed to determine utilization liability is the diagnosis of the condition and the procedures necessary to cure or elevate the disease. In this chapter, I discuss the problems inherent to diagnostic coding on insurance claims.

INTERNATIONAL CLASSIFICATION OF DISEASE

The diagnostic coding process uses a text reference called the *ICD9CM*, which stands for International Classification of Disease 9th Modification Clinical Module. It is more commonly known as the ICD codebook. The codebook is traceable to the early works of a pioneer epidemiologist, Dr. John Graunt. Working in 17th century London, England, Graunt was pivotal in determining disease origins from contaminated water sources.[1] His collection of data from the London mortality bills established a pattern of incidence of disease stemming from a tainted water supply. Interestingly enough, these mortality statistics later became important in the business of life insurance.[2] Today, the *ICD9CM* codebook is accepted internationally as a standard text for the classification of disease. It can be extremely accurate when used by someone experienced or trained in coding diseases.

PROBLEMS WITH CURRENT METHODS OF DIAGNOSTIC CODING

A statement in the introduction of the *ICD9CM* manual claims, "This version precisely delineates the clinical picture of each patient, providing exact information beyond that needed for statistical groupings and analysis of healthcare trends."[3] But what trends are being measured and what is the value of this measurement? The answer involves incidence. Incidence measures the risk of disease developing within a defined population.[4] Unfortunately, this measurement is not enough to allow insurance carriers to predict true utilization. As defined in the previous chapter, utilization is a function of length of stay due to the chronicity of the illness and the costs associated with it. The data that insurance carriers need to predict disease chronicity relate to burden or prevalence.[5]

The practice of relying an incidence data collected via claim forms has made utilization prediction in the managed care or capitated care markets hazardous. Understanding this will bring home the importance of in-office data collection and analysis. Data relayed to an insurance company on HCFA 1500 and UB82 claim forms can only statistically measure the number of times a diagnosis happened during a specified time period within a defined population. The data on these forms do not relate to the burden of illness—how sick those with the disease are—or to the chronicity associated with disease.

In addition, the diagnostic coding system does not reflect complicating factors, severity of illness, or the co-morbitities of the disease process to adequately allow accurate data capture for measurement of the burden of illness. Thus, the burden and the chronicity of illness are not reflected in the coding process. These two factors reflect an enormous statistical problem for predicting the utilization rate of a population. Therefore, data used by insurance carriers as a basis of managed care and capitation utilization prediction contain an enormous amount of error.

Other Sources of Coding Bias

However, the data problems do not only affect insurance carriers. The inaccuracies and lack of information are also contained in the medical and financial records of providers wishing to contract. Prior to managed care or capitated contracting, providers must understand other sources of coding bias, reconstitute data, and then produce accurate in-office statistics that reflect real utilization experience.

I was aware of other sources of coding bias in my own office, but I felt compelled to confirm that other offices represented similar sources of bias. So, in preparation for this book, I spent time surveying a wide variety of offices in the Southern California area, including multispeciality, single specialty, solo, and group practices. I spoke with the people who performed the insurance coding in those offices. They were extremely open with their answers, with most showing no embarrassment in admitting that they "played the coding game." I suppose this was because such games are so well accepted within the industry.

The first generalization I drew from my survey is that although physicians make the diagnoses, their staff members most likely do the coding. Physicians and most, if not all, staffs have little or no formal training in coding. Any training received is either self-taught from coding manuals or learned from short seminars.

Staffs tend to use a general diagnosis code to avoid trapping themselves into a diagnostic box; that is, committing to a more specific evaluation that might justify only a short length of stay. They hope a more general code will achieve a longer length of stay. They also tend to supply the code the insurance company is most likely to pay, even though a more accurate code could apply. An example would be the use of an ill-defined diagnosis as displacement of the lumbar intervertebral disc, rather than lumbar spine strain or sprain.

Additionally, specialists tend to use a narrower range of codes, giving the appearance of a pattern of diagnosis and treatment. This abbreviated list of ICD codes produces a treatment pattern reflecting great variance in response times for similar diagnoses, which otherwise are not adjusted for complicating factors, severity of illness, and co-morbidities.

CPT Coding

In addition to the ICD codes received from providers, insurance companies also receive information on treatment plans. This information is relayed by the current procedural terminology (CPT) coding system. I will cover CPT coding in more detail in Chapter 4, but here I would like to point out that the system has several problems similar to those found in the ICD coding system.

In particular, medical staffs and providers tend to avoid modifiers, unlisted codes, or procedures designated by report (BR), because of the time, effort, and delay in reimbursement. As a result, staffs tend to use other higher or lower codes to avoid the reimbursement delays caused by use of possibly more accurate CPT codes. This process is known as *upcoding* or *downcoding*.

But the primary problems in CPT coding stem from poor understanding of a new section in the coding manual that addresses entitled evaluation and management. The procedure described in this section has the potential to correctly measure the amount of work needed to perform evaluation and management of diseases, but most people so poorly implement it as to render it nearly useless. In the next chapter, I will discuss how to consistently and accurately use the evaluation and management CPT codes.

A treatment plan represented by procedure coding is justified by the diagnosis; that is, without an established diagnosis, a treatment plan is not necessary. Thus, the diagnosis becomes the driving force behind the procedures used in the treatment plan, the length of stay associated with the treatment plan, and finally the costs associated with the disease that was diagnosed.

THE DIAGNOSTIC PROCESS

Before we can correct the problem of data capture, it will be helpful to discuss how the diagnostic process works. As a patient enters the examination room, the physician listens to the chief complaint. He or she decides what is the most likely reason for these complaints and next elicits a patient history to eliminate unlikely causes of these symptoms.

Becoming more convinced of a likely cause, the physician elects a standard series of tests with sufficient sensitivity and specificity to prove his or her causation theory. As you can guess, this is not always a perfect procedure. Most patients with difficult diseases to diagnose are often moved up the testing ladder until enough differential diagnoses have been performed to leave only a small number of possible diseases that can cause the symptoms. (This is also why the last doctor you see always appears to be the smartest, leaving you to wonder why you didn't go to him or her first.)

This process of determining the causes of the symptoms can become complex. Experience makes it easier and more exact. However, an exploration of the most simple and probably the most common diagnosis given—strain and sprain—can indicate just how complicated data capture and accurate diagnosis coding can be.

The diagnosis of strain and sprain can probably be applied to at least 80 percent of all orthopedic diagnoses. It is frequently used as a working diagnosis when a different, more accurate one is suspected but not yet confirmed. It is what most insurance companies receive as a primary diagnosis, and most offices rarely update it on the claim form, so it tends to remain as the prime driver for most orthopedic claims.

The example of strain and sprain might seem to be exceedingly simple; but an examination of the problems associated with it will suggest how a more complex diagnostic entity can provide an even greater problem in data collection and measure.

To begin with, confusion exists among many practitioners as to what tissue strain or sprain pertain. Sprain is commonly misunderstood to apply to tears, and strain to overstretching. This is even more confusing if you should examine Dorland's dictionary, which defines strain as to overexercise, to overuse to an extreme and harmful degree. The same reference defines sprain as a joint injury in which some of the fibers of a supporting ligament are ruptured, but the continuity of the ligament remains intact.[6]

Such confusion exists over these simple terms that the AMA committee on sports medicine clarified the definitions. As it stands today, both terms mean overstretching and tearing, but strains apply to muscle-tendon units, whereas sprains apply to ligaments.[7] But the difficulties with diagnostic coding go beyond simple definitions. Diagnostic coding is especially deficient in addressing severity.

Sprains come in three degrees of severity: mild, moderate, and severe. These are also known as first, second, and third degree. First-degree sprains, which most of us have experienced, require little or no treatment. The eversion-type ankle sprain is the most common. In this type of first-degree sprain, the majority of ligamentous fibers remain intact. The exact number is unknown, but it is estimated that 20 to 30 percent of the fibers tear in an eversion sprain, leaving 70 to 80 percent of the ligament intact, which gives the joint its residual stability.

Determining the amount of intact ligamentous fibers is the primary aim of stability assessment in orthopedics. Most such assessments involve a series of provocative maneuvers that test stability from a variety or combination of directions. The reason is that multiple ligaments usually originate from an area, thus several directions of forces or orthopedic maneuvers may be needed to isolate and assess the integrity of the tissue being tested.

Because of the degree of difficulty in properly isolating an individual ligament, these tests and maneuvers involve a degree of subjectivity. This can translate into errors in the diagnosis. The subsequent coding of such errors further translates into variance in utilization predictions. Of course, in our example of ankle sprain not many doctors will be far wrong; but in more complex situations, the chance of diagnostic error multiplies.

Thus, diagnostic errors result from two prime factors: the sensitivity and the specificity of the testing strategy being used to diagnose the condition. Sensitivity relates to how much disease must be present before the test can detect it. Specificity is the degree of accuracy with which the testing strategy can identify a certain disease.

Technology can minimize sensitivity and specificity errors. Many currently used technologies have problems of sensitivity and specificity that affect utilization. For example, a common technology used in orthopedic testing is plain film x-rays. The sensitivity rating for the use of such x-rays in detecting missing bone mass is low. As much as 60 percent of the bone mass may be missing before traditional plain film can detect it. Moreover, conditions such as osteoporosis, infection, and cancer may be present and not be detected by plain x-rays because of this sensitivity problem.

Plain film sensitivity compares poorly with the sensitivity of a bone scan, which can predict as little as 2 percent of bone-mass loss. Bone scans are of poor specificity, however, as they can tell only where change to bone is happening, not the cause of the disease. In contrast, plain film may show an identifiable change in bone appearance, making the specificity of plain x-ray film superior to a bone scan.

This overlap of differing sensitivities and specificities in testing strategies is why the cost of testing often rises; it also accounts for the seeming redundancy in testing. Providers must weigh the benefits of what is learned from particular testing strategies against the cost and hazards of using them. For example, typical orthopedic maneuvers and tests cannot isolate to a single tissue, giving them a low degree of specificity. Of course, more accurate imaging techniques do exist, but they are more costly and also may not lead the physician to alter treatment. Remember, providers must use cost-effective measures.

I'll skip secondary sprains for a moment for a quick look at third-degree sprains. In these situations, the ligament has been completely severed; that is, the ligament is not contiguous, it is 100 percent torn. The joint is wildly unstable as the retaining purpose of the ligament is completely violated. These injuries require surgical intervention for reattachment.

By definition, second-degree sprains can involve the tearing of about 30 to 99 percent of the fibers. This produces a differential clinical picture. The stability is subjective, but ascertainable to a degree. Possible stability tests include the other imaging techniques such as stress plain films or, in more severe cases, direct examination of the joint through a scope.

The differential testing process therefore has much room for error. Even the terminology of first, second, and third degree has deficiencies, particularly as it pertains to the large second-degree-category. To account for this large definitional variance, additional second-degree sprain modifiers have been used, such as severely moderate or mildly moderate.

Degree of severity and recovery time are linked. Usually, the greater the degree of severity, the longer the healing time. As can be seen by the previous discussion, the assessment of the degree of injury is important in determining the prognosis, length of stay, and utilization.

Typically, the recovery time for middle-of-the-road, second-degree injuries takes six to eight weeks, but this depends on other factors. The patient may have an underlying bone pathology or may be nutritionally deficient, which could lengthen response time. He or she may not protect or rest the area, which could also delay, if not prevent, proper healing. The patient may have a systemic illness, such as diabetes, that may dramatically impact the response time. In short, many other factors, which at first glance may not seem to have an impact, can affect healing time.

As we can see, the use of the simple diagnostic terms *strain* and *sprain* offer poor value to an insurance company in predicting response, prognosis, and utilization. Additionally, other factors, unaccounted for in diagnostic coding, affect response time and thus costs.

DIAGNOSTIC STRUCTURING

The only way to minimize errors in data collection is to control them. The problem is that many of the factors affecting diagnostic entities are not known. As such, it is incumbent upon those in the front lines of healthcare and healthcare research to delineate them.

One way to eliminate or minimize data collection errors is to use a diagnostically structured statement. This allows more accurate and consistent in-office data collection. The format of a diagnostically structured statement is easily understood by physicians and easily taught to staffs. In addition, the basic structure of the statement is flexible enough to allow modification for individual medical specialties. It also facilitates retrospective review of files and diagnostic statements to determine past utilization behaviors. This system accounts for additional data elements that affect utilization variance.

To demonstrate how this can be done, I will use a method I have named *diagnostic structuring*, and, for ease of explanation, I will continue to use the example of the strain and sprain diagnostic entity.

Diagnostic structuring has four primary parts:

1. Dynamic of injury.
2. Tissue of causation.
3. Attendant factors.
4. Complicating factors.

The *dynamic of injury* is how the present complaints came to attention. Specifically, disease comes about in two ways: as the result of accident or illness. Information on the dynamic of injury is most useful in predicting utilization when combined with other information. For example, the complaint of back pain in a 65-year-old man always suggests ominous possibilities. After discriminating between traumatic back pain (accident) and an insidious onset (illness), a physician would likely lean toward trauma as the probable cause of the pain, especially if a history of trauma or overuse is present, thus avoiding the expensive additional testing needed in diagnosing the more ominous clinical picture of insidious onset.

The second element of diagnostic structure is the *tissue of causation*. This is the tissue, or system, that the testing strategy has led the physician to diagnose as aberrant. Obviously, the more accurate the identification of the causative tissue, the more accurate the treatment, prognosis, and determination of utilization.

Refer again to the ankle sprain, the most common ligamentous injury to the body. Compare the prognosis, cost implications, and anticipated response time of a first-degree ankle sprain to those of a third-degree sprain. First-degree sprains are self-resolving, whereas third-degree sprains require surgery. (Remember, all of these sprains can be and usually are identified with the same ICD code. Expert coders write in degree of injury; but these handwritten modifications are left out when the diagnosis is rekeyed at the insurance company. Additionally, some providers submit electronic claims (e-claims). However, e-claim computers only take the first diagnosis and ignore the rest. This is why people are taught to place the most severe diagnostic code first.)

The third element of the diagnostic structure is *attendant factors*. Attendant factors are the subjective complaints, usually pain. An example would be headache, low-back pain, and sciatica (leg pain). The tendency to submit a pain diagnosis is high. When I taught insurance coding I would ask students, "From the diagnostic information submitted to the insurance carrier, how long do you think the insurance carrier will give you to fix pain?" The answer is, the carrier won't give you any time; diagnostic coding of pain only precipitates the inevitable request for additional information from the insurance carrier.

Attendant factors give insight to the level of subjectivity of the patient, but they are not as important in utilization prediction as they are in monitoring patient progress, studying outcomes, or comparing subjective consistency with other patients with similar diagnoses.

Years of listening to subjective complaints have left most physicians callous as to the reliability of such patient-provided data. However, there is a method of collecting subjective complaints that will reliably standardize them. This collection method allows for comparison of complaints, making them ratable and thus more consistent and reliable in data calculations.

The system I use for standardizing subjective complaints is based on the one outlined in the *California Worker's Compensation Guidelines*.[8] But all the states use similar systems. In this system, subjective complaints have two components: frequency and intensity.

The concept of frequency is easy to gauge since nearly everyone understands time. Four general categories of time are used:

1. Intermittent.
2. Occasional.
3. Frequent.
4. Constant.

Intermittent, occasional, frequent, and constant stand for 25, 50, 75, and 100 percent of the time, respectively. (Note that the system outlined in the American Medical Association's *Guide to the Evaluation of Permanent Impairment*[9] reverses the ratings of intermittent and occasional from those specified in the California system. California rates occasional as 25 percent; the A.M.A. rates it as 50 percent.)

The intensity of pain is best understood as a function of precluded activity or handicap. There are four degrees of handicap: slight, mild, moderate, and severe. (The California worker's compensation system acknowledges a fifth category: minimal pain. However, this type of pain is not compensable.) A slight pain offers no handicap and the patient can perform the task that precipitated the pain. A mild pain is one in which an individual can complete the task that precipitated the pain with only minor exception as to how it is performed. With moderate pain, the individual can complete the task, but only with a major exception or handicap as to how it is performed. Severe pain totally precludes the patient from performing the task.

Using this system, a provider can identify when symptoms are inconsistent with diagnostic entities. For example, a first-degree ankle sprain would not be consistent with reported constant severe pain. Other factors of injury or perhaps emotional issues could explain the discrepancy.

(This subjective rating system will become more important as America moves toward full compliance with the Americans with Disabilities Act (ADA). The ADA is meant to protect those with impairment. A major criterion for impairment is impact on lifestyle. But the ADA has no ratable factors of disabilities; assessing an injury's impact on daily lifestyle will be difficult without formal functional studies. I suggest that use of a consistent language, such as the one found in this subjective rating system, will reduce problems and variances in future ADA claims.)

The fourth element of the structure of a diagnosis consists of *complicating factors*. They are very important in data capture and utilization prediction. Complicating factors are those that slow down response times or worsen the healing process. These factors are subdivided into three categories:

1. Environmental.
2. Pathological.
3. Co-morbidity.

An individual may have none of these factors, one of these, several expressions of one, all, or any combination of these. The healthcare industry does not have a list of specific factors within these categories. Nor does it have data on their impact on utilization. But many complicating factors are suspected. Some, such as the use of alcohol and smoking during pregnancy, are rather well known. Others are yet undiscovered. It will become incumbent on the group in control of utilization to discover these relationships. In the capitated market, this will be the provider of healthcare, the physician.

Complicating factors that are environmental in nature include lifestyle and job activities. For examples, a patient may aggravate a poorly healed ankle sprain by being overweight; or someone may prolong an ankle injury through continual use because of occupational demands. Or it may be simply a patient who doesn't follow directions.

Another extremely important environmental factor is age. It takes no great insight to foresee why a 90-year-old person will take longer to heal than a 23-year-old. Occupational medicine deals daily with environmental reasons for the chronicity of disease and illness in the workplace.

The second category of complicating factors results from pathological processes that are directly involved in the diagnosed disease. An example would be discovering the presence of a congenital abnormality called *spondlolythesis* when treating a low-back disc condition. (A spondylolysis is an interruption of a structurally supportive portion of the lumbar vertebrae called the *pars interarticularis*). This condition is thought to predispose a person to low-back pain.

The third category is co-morbidity. These are conditions that coexist with the disease being treated. They may become very complex and are closely related to the pathological factors previously discussed. However, I feel that co-morbid processes differ from pathological complicating factors in that the latter are directly involved in the consideration of a treatment plan. In the example of the low-back condition with spondlolythesis, the presence of the spondlolythesis offers a continuing problem with the management of the primary diagnosis.

In contrast, consider the following example of a co-morbid process. Say a patient with diabetes is being treated for an ankle sprain, but the diabetes is compromising the circulation in the affected leg. Although it is involved in slowing or delaying response time of the sprain, and is a consideration in formulating a treatment plan, diabetes is a diagnostic entity to itself and a separate process independent of the primary condition being treated.

Figure 3–1 presents an outline of elements involved in a diagnostically structured statement. Consistent use of a formal diagnostically structured statement will result in more consistent data

FIGURE 3–1

Diagnostic Structure

1. Dynamic of injury
   a. Accident
   b. Illness

2. Tissue of causation—Discovered through diagnostic testing that is both as sensitive and specific as reasonably possible or necessary.

3. Attendant factors—Subjective complaints that are the result of a disease tissue or organ system, complete with specific modifiers as to duration, length, and severity.

4. Complicating factors
   a. Environmental—Age, socioeconomic, habits, and attitudes of health.
   b. Pathological—Closely tied processes which directly affect the chief complaint and require concurrent management. These include congenital and developmental abnormalities.
   c. Co-morbidity—Concurrent conditions that affect the primary complaint and are separate and distinct diagnostic entities with their own clinical course.

capture. Comparison of similar conditions provides the basis for speculation and research into new areas of medical relationships between concurrent problems.

Through the use of a diagnostically structured statement, a completed example of a low-back injury might look like this:

> The patient is suffering from a trauma-induced left-lateral L5/S1 disk prolapse with attendant frequent moderate grade 3 [meaning to the level of the foot] left-sided sciatic radiation, constant moderate back pain, grade 3 muscle spasm, and occasional urinary incontinence, which is further complicated by obesity.

This statement gives great insight as to the disease, including quantified information on severity and level of subjective complaints, and a complicating factor that affects outcomes, management options, and ultimately cost. It will be helpful to hold meetings with physicians and staff to determine those suspected complicating factors and agree upon the final diagnostic structure adopted.

REFERENCES

1. A. S. Lyons and R. J. Petrucelli, *Medicine, An Illustrated Text* (New York: 1978) Abraham Press; and J. Morgan, *Concise Epidemiology, A Practical Text*, 3rd ed., (Loma Linda, CA: MDM Consulting, 1994).

2. Lyons and Petrucelli, *Medicine*, p. 463.

3. *ICD9CM* (Chicago: American Medical Association, 1987).

4. Morgan, *Concise Epidemiology.*

5. *Ibid.*

6. *Dorland's Illustrated Medical Dictionary*, 25th ed. (Philadelphia: W. B. Saunders, 1965).

7. Don O'Donoghue, *Treatment of Injuries to Athletes*, 3rd ed. (Philadelphia: W. B. Saunders, 1976), p. 62.

8. *California Worker's Compensation Guidelines.*

9. *Guide to the Evaluation of Permanent Impairment*, 3rd ed. (Chicago: American Medical Association, 1971).

4 CHAPTER

Differential Diagnosis and CPT Coding

Current procedural terminology, or CPT, is the basis for coding treatment procedures. The CPT coding manual has six procedural sections, five of which address specialties; the other presents examination codes used for evaluation and management, or E/M (see Figure 4–1). The five sections for specialty procedures detail specific codes for anesthesiology, surgery, pathology and laboratory, radiology, and medicine. But there is overlap. A provider may use codes other than those specified for his or her speciality; for the most part, however, most specialists use few codes from other sections. This large specialty division of the codebook is rather straightforward; the codes are well defined and tend to change little from year to year. The evaluation and management section is more problematic.

Providers do make mistakes with the specialty codes; and there are advantages to be gained from certain code selections. But it is not my purpose to do an in-depth exploration of the individual speciality procedure sections of the CPT codebook. I prefer to discuss the use of a differential diagnosis in proper E/M code selection and the impact it has on collection of utilization data.

EVALUATION AND MANAGEMENT CODES

The evaluation and management section is the newest major change in the CPT codebook. It replaces the 9700 coding system, a time-based system used to code examinations and office visits. In an indemnity insurance financing system, providers tend to use higher codes than are necessary to justify higher fees, which pro-

FIGURE 4–1

CPT Code Manual Major Subdivisions

Evaluation and management (E/M)	1st major division
Anesthesiology	
Surgery	
Pathology and laboratory	2nd major division
Radiology	
Medicine	

duces biased data. The data collected as a result of this "upcoding" indicate longer time allotments for evaluation and management of patients with a given disease than were actually needed. That is, current data lead to artificially inflated utilization times. In a practical setting, this bias could result in an administrator hiring too many doctors or feeling that a capitation rate is too low because it will take more time to evaluate and manage a particular patient pool.

Health services researcher William Hsiao developed the CPT evaluation and management codes in an attempt to reflect the actual work needed to treat patients. It was thought that proper use of these codes would minimize variation and make selection more consistent with case severity. Unfortunately, the E/M code system is too complex for most doctors, coders, and insurance adjusters to understand. As a result, most "cross-walk" from their old fee schedules, picking a code they think justifies a fee they prefer.

The E/M code system, properly used, is accurate; it's just not well understood. In addition, the coding is so difficult to audit that most insurance companies tend not to review E/M code selection except for the most complex cases. Even then, review is usually performed only to reduce the fee associated with it rather than to dispute what the code represents.

As a result of its complexity, the general lack of understanding, and lack of audits, this new system is also subject to the coding game, as was the 9700 system. For example, the California worker's compensation fee schedule only sparingly uses complex codes such as 99205. However, many providers circumvent this restriction by using a modifier of -52, meaning a lesser examination. This reduces their fee by a small amount, thus avoiding audit or denial. This new round of the coding game is producing more inaccurate data. This data bias affects both the in-office data and insurance carrier data. To correct this bias, providers need to understand what it takes to make proper E/M code selections.

MAKING CORRECT E/M CODING CHOICES

To reach a code decision using the E/M coding system, providers must consider three components, as shown in the following equation:

History + Examination + Medical decision making =
E/M code choice

These three components are then further subdivided into four sub-divisions, which represent escalating complexity (see Figure 4–2). The labels for the increasing levels of complexity for *history* and *examination* are the same. They are problem focused, expanded problem focus, detailed, and comprehensive. Although there is similarity in the labels, the requirement for each level of complexity is different. The labels for the increasing levels of complexity for *medical decision making* are straightforward, low complexity, moderate complexity, and high complexity.

Requirements for Selection of Level of Complexity for History

The requirements for each of the four levels of history increase as complexity increases. These include chief complaint; history of illness; system review; and past, family, and social history. These four elements are added and expanded as the level of complexity rises. Examine Figure 4–3 carefully.

Problem focused is the lowest level of history. Justification of the problem-focused level of history requires a chief complaint and a brief history of the present problem. But exactly what is meant by a brief history? What may be a brief history to one physician may not be brief to another.

To standardize the history-taking process, I suggest that providers use a common format such as the one that Dr. Barbara Bates presented in *A Guide to Physical Examination and History Tak-*

FIGURE 4–2

Levels of Complexity for the Three Components of E/M Code Selection

History	Examination	Medical Decision Making
Problem focused	Problem focused	Straightforward
Expanded problem focused	Expanded problem focused	Low complexity
Detailed	Detailed	Moderate complexity
Comprehensive	Comprehensive	High complexity

FIGURE 4-3

Requirements for Selection of Level of Complexity for History

Problem focused
  Chief complaint
  Brief history of present problem

Expanded problem focused
  Chief complaint
  Brief history of problem
  Problem-pertinent system review

Detailed
  Chief complaint
  History of problem (becomes extended)
  System review (becomes extended)
  Pertinent past, family, and/or social history

Comprehensive
  Chief complaint
  History of problem
  System review (becomes complete)
  Past, family, and social history (becomes complete)

ing. Figure 4–4 reproduces this comprehensive history, which I believe to be a perfect format for all of the various levels of histories.

The first six items in Bates's comprehensive history define nicely the brief history required for the problem-focused level (see Figure 4–5). The histories required for higher levels of complexity can follow Bates's format, using more of the outline. For the level of expanded problem focused, for example, the CPT codebook adds the requirement of a problem-pertinent system review to those already given for problem focused. The first column of Figure 4–6 lists the system review used by Bates and the systems; the second column lists those suggested in 1996 CPT codebook. It is interesting to note that the CPT codebook divides the system review into body areas and organ systems. These become even more important later in determining examination levels.

The detailed level builds on the requirements of the expanded problem focused by extending history and system review and adding a pertinent past, family, and/or social history. Finally, the

F I G U R E 4–4

Comprehensive History: Adult Patient

Date of history

Identifying data, including age, sex, race, place of birth, marital status, occupation, and religion.

Source of referral, if any, and the purpose of it.

Source of history, such as the patient, a relative, a friend, the patient's medical record, or a referral letter.

Reliability, if relevant.

Chief complaints, when possible in the patient's own words: "My stomach hurts and I feel awful." Sometimes patients have no overt complaints; ascertain their goals instead. "I have come for my regular checkup" or "I've been admitted for a thorough evaluation of my heart."

Present illness. This is a clear, chronological narrative account of the problems for which the patient is seeking care. It should include the onset of the problem, the setting in which it developed, its manifestations, and any past treatments. The principal symptoms should be described in terms of (1) location, (2) quality, (3) quantity or severity, (4) timing (i.e., onset, duration, and frequency), (5) the setting in which they occur, (6) factors that have aggravated or relieved them, and (7) associated manifestations. Relevant data from the patient's chart, such as laboratory reports, also belong in the present illness, as do significant negatives (i.e., the absence of certain symptoms that will aid in differential diagnosis).

   A present illness should also include patients' responses to their own symptoms and incapacities. What does the patient think has caused the problem? What are the underlying worries that have led to seeking professional attention? ("I think I may have appendicitis.") And why is that a worry? ("My Uncle Charlie died of a ruptured appendix.") Further, what effects has the illness had on the patient's life? This question is especially important in understanding a patient with chronic illness. "What can't you do now that you could do before? How has the backache, shortness of breath, or whatever, affected your ability to work? Your life at home? Your social activities? Your role as a parent? Your role as a husband, or wife? The way you feel about yourself as a man, or a woman?"

Past history

   General state of health as the patient perceives it.

   Childhood illnesses, such as measles, rubella, mumps, whooping cough, chicken pox, rheumatic fever, scarlet fever, polio.

   Adult illnesses.

   Psychiatric illnesses.

F I G U R E   4–4 (*continued*)

Accidents and injuries.

Operations.

Hospitalizations not already described.

Current health status. Although some of the variables grouped under this heading have past as well as current components, they all have potential impact on current health and possible health-related interventions.

Allergies.

Immunizations, such as tetanus, pertussis, diphtheria, polio, measles, rubella, mumps, influenza, hepatitis B, *Hemophilus influenzae,* type b, and pneumococcal vaccine.

Screening tests appropriate to the patient's age, such as hematocrits, urinalyses, tuberculin tests, Pap smears, mammograms, stools for occult blood, and cholesterol tests, together with the results and the dates they were last performed.

Environmental hazards, including those in the home, school, and workplace.

Use of safety measures, such as seat belts and other methods related to specific hazards.

Exercise and leisure activities.

Sleep patterns, including times that the person goes to bed and awakens, daytime naps, and any difficulties in falling asleep or staying asleep.

Diet, including all the dietary intake for a recent 24-hour period, and any dietary restrictions or supplements. Be specific in your questions. "Take yesterday, for example. Starting from when you woke up, what did you eat or drink first? Then what? And then?" Ask specifically about coffee, tea, cola drinks, and other caffeine-containing beverages.

Current medications, including home remedies, nonprescription drugs, vitamin/mineral supplements, and medicines borrowed from family or friends. When a patient seems likely to be taking one or more medications, survey one 24-hour period in detail. "Let's look at yesterday. Starting from when you woke up, what was the first medicine you took? How much? How often in the day did you take it? What are you taking it for? What other medicines?"

Tobacco, including the type (smoked, e.g., cigarettes, or smokeless, e.g., chewing tobacco or snuff), amount, and duration of use (e.g., cigarettes, a pack a day for 12 years).

Alcohol, drugs, and related substances.

Family history. The age and health, or age and cause of death, of each immediate family member (i.e., parents, siblings, spouse, and children). Data on grandparents or grandchildren may also be useful.

F I G U R E 4–4 (*continued*)

The occurrence within the family or any of the following conditions: diabetes, tuberculosis, heart disease, high blood pressure, stroke, kidney disease, cancer, arthritis, anemia, headaches, epilepsy, mental illness, alcoholism, drug addiction, and symptoms like those of the patient.

Psychosocial history. This is an outline or narrative description that captures the important and relevant information about the patient as a person:

Home situation and significant others. "Who lives at home with you? Tell me a little about them, and about your friends." "Who helps you when you are sick, or need assistance?"

Daily life, from the time of arising to bedtime. "What is a typical day like? What do you do first? Next?"

Important experiences, including upbringing, schooling, military service, job history, financial situation, marriage, recreation, retirement.

Religious beliefs relevant to perceptions of health, illness, and treatment.

The patient's outlook on the present and on the future.

Review of systems

General. Usual weight, recent weight change, any clothes that fit tighter or looser than before. Weakness, fatigue, fever.

Skin. Rashes, lumps, sores, itching, dryness, color change, changes in hair or nails.

Head. Headache, head injury.

Eyes. Vision, glasses or contact lenses, last eye examination, pain, redness, excessive tearing, double vision, blurred vision, spots or specks, glaucoma, cataracts.

Ears. Hearing, tinnitus, vertigo, earaches, infection, discharge. If hearing is decreased, use of hearing aids.

Nose and sinuses. Frequent colds; nasal stuffiness, discharge, or itching; hay fever, nosebleeds, sinus trouble.

Mouth and throat. Condition of teeth and gums, bleeding gums, dentures, if any, and how they fit, last dental examination, sore tongue, dry mouth, frequent sore throats, hoarseness.

Neck. Lumps, "swollen glands," goiter, pain or stiffness in the neck.

Breasts. Lumps, pain or discomfort, nipple discharge, self-examination.

Respiratory. Cough, sputum (color, quantity), hemoptysis, wheezing, asthma, bronchitis, emphysema, pneumonia, tuberculosis, pleurisy; last chest x-ray film.

Cardiac. Heart trouble, high blood pressure, rheumatic fever, heart murmurs,

FIGURE 4-4 (*concluded*)

chest pain or discomfort, palpitations; dyspnea, orthopnea, paroxysmal nocturnal dyspnea, edema; past electrocardiogram or other heart tests.

Gastrointestinal. Trouble swallowing, heartburn, appetite, nausea, vomiting, regurgitation, vomiting of blood, indigestion. Frequency of bowel movements, color and size of stools, change in bowel habits, rectal bleeding or black tarry stools, hemorrhoids, constipation, diarrhea. Abdominal pain, food intolerance, excessive belching or passing of gas. Jaundice, liver or gallbladder trouble, hepatitis.

Urinary. Frequency of urination, polyuria, nocturia, burning or pain on urination, hematuria, urgency, reduced caliber or force of the urinary stream, hesitancy, dribbling, incontinence; urinary infections, stones.

Genital—Male. Hernias; discharge from or sores on the penis, testicular pain or masses, history of sexually transmitted diseases and their treatments. Sexual preference, interest, function, satisfaction, and problems.

Genital—Female. Age at menarche; regularity, frequency, and duration of periods; amount of bleeding, bleeding between periods or after intercourse, last menstrual period; dysmenorrhea, premenstrual tension; age at menopause, menopausal symptoms, postmenopausal bleeding. If the patient was born before 1971, exposure to DES (diethylstilbestrol) from maternal use during pregnancy. Discharge, itching, sores, lumps, sexually transmitted diseases and their treatments. Number of pregnancies, number of deliveries, number of abortions (spontaneous and induced), complications of pregnancy; birth control methods. Sexual preference, interest, function, satisfaction; any problems, including dyspareunia.

Peripheral vascular. Intermittent claudication, leg cramps, varicose veins, past clots in the veins.

Musculoskeletal. Muscle or joint pains, stiffness, arthritis, gout, backache. If present, describe location and symptoms (e.g., swelling, redness, pain, tenderness, stiffness, weakness, limitation of motion or activity).

Neurologic. Fainting, blackouts, seizures, weakness, paralysis, numbness or loss of sensation, tingling or "pins and needles," tremors or other involuntary movements.

Hematologic. Anemia, easy bruising or bleeding, past transfusions and any reactions to them.

Endocrine. Thyroid trouble, heat or cold intolerance, excessive sweating; diabetes, excessive thirst or hunger, polyuria.

Psychiatric. Nervousness, tension, mood including depression, memory.

comprehensive level is almost the same as detailed except the system review and past, family, and social history both become complete; the *or* is eliminated from the requirement of past, family

FIGURE 4-5

Criteria for Brief History

1. Date of history
2. Identifying data—age sex, race, place of birth, marital status, occupation.
3. Source of referral—if any.
4. Source of history—patient, relative, friend, medical records.
5. Chief complaint
6. Present illness—location, quality, severity, timing, precipating factors, aggravating or relieving factors, associated manifestations.

FIGURE 4-6

System Review Comparison

Bates	CPT
General (weight changes, etc.)	
Skin	Skin*
Head	Head, including face
Eyes	Eyes*
Ears	Ears, nose, mouth, and throat*
Nose and sinuses	
Mouth and throat	
Neck	Neck
Breast	Chest, including breast and axilla
Respiratory	Respiratory*
Cardiac	Cardiovascular*
Gastrointestinal	Gastrointestinal*
Urinary	
Genital	Genitalia, groin, and buttocks
Perpherial vascular	
Musculoskeletal	Musculoskeletal*
Neurologic	Neurologic*
Hematologic	Immunologic/lymphatic/hematologic*
Endrocrine	
Psychriatic	Psychiatric*
	Back
	Abdomen
	Each extremity

* Denotes CPT-designated organ system.

and/or social history. The differences will become clearer with a review of Figure 4–3.

Requirements for Selection of Level of Complexity for Examination

Examination fairly closely follows history in its pattern of escalating severity and complexity. The basic level of examination is problem focused. It requires an examination of the affected part or organ system, as shown in Figure 4–7. The increasing levels build on that. The organ systems are marked with an asterisk in Figure 4–6. Obviously, if a provider examines more than one organ system or body area, a higher code would be in order. There is room for interpretation and room to upcode. However, to prepare for capitation and collect accurate data it may be necessary to determine the extent of the examination in-office or by committee. This will help standardize data collection. The level of the work being performed to evaluate and manage a patient with a diagnosis must be understood in order to measure performance.

The next level of examination is expanded problem focused. It builds on the requirements for problem focused by adding examination of other symptomatic or related organ systems. The third level is the detailed examination. It extends the examination to multiple areas or organs and to the other symptomatic or related organ systems.

The final last level is the comprehensive examination. It is a

---

FIGURE 4–7

Requirements for Selection of Level of Examination Complexity

> *Problem focused*—Examination limited to the affected part or organ system.
>
> *Expanded problem focused*—Examination limited to the affected area or organ and other symptomatic or related organ systems.
>
> D*etailed*—Extended examination of the affected areas or organs and other symptomatic or related organ systems.
>
> *Comprehensive*—Complete single-system speciality or complete multisystem examination.

complete single-system specialty or a complete multisystem examination.

Requirements for Selection of Level of Complexity for Decision Making

Decision making is the most complex component of E/M code selection. Although there are only four levels of decision—straightforward, low, moderate, and high complexity—each has three components:

1. Number of diagnoses or management options.
2. Amount and/or complexity of data to be reviewed.
3. Risk of complications and/or morbidity or mortality.

Further, each of these three components has four different requirements. Figure 4–8 presents these components and requirements in what is the framework of a choice chart for medical decision making. As the discussion proceeds, I'll complete the chart by adding necessary coding information in subsequent figures.

I feel the need to summarize since all of these subdivisions and levels can become confusing. First, it takes three specific levels

FIGURE 4–8

Foundation of Choice Chart for Medical Decision Making

Number of Diagnoses or Management Options	Amount and/or Complexity of Data to Be Reviewed	Risk of Complications and/or Morbidity or Mortality	Type of Decision Making
Minimal	Minimal or none	Minimal	Straightforward
Limited	Limited	Low	Low complexity
Multiple	Moderate	Moderate	Moderate complexity
Extensive	Extensive	Extensive	High complexity

to justify an E/M code. These levels are history, examination, and medical decision making.

Further, history and examination each have four levels of complexity, and these levels are identified by the same levels: problem focused, expanded problem focused, detailed, and comprehensive. Each of these levels of complexity have different requirements.

Medical decision making has four levels of complexity. However, each level is justified by three components: (1) number of diagnoses or management options; (2) amount and/or complexity of data to be reviewed; and (3) risk of complications and/or morbidity or mortality.

Number of Diagnoses or Management Options

The selection of the proper number of diagnoses or management options is a function of the number of the body areas or organ systems, as listed in Figure 4–6, that were examined. This also relates to isolation of the causative tissue, as discussed in Chapter 3. Coding subjective complaints leads to inaccurate data. For example, the diagnosis of chest pain will justify a two-day stay in the hospital, but it adds little to data collection since the causative problem or etiology of chest pain can vary from rib pain or gastroesophageal reflux to a serious cardiovascular incident.

For further clarification, let's refer to take the diagnostic statement offered at the end of the previous chapter:

> The patient is suffering from a trauma-induced left-lateral L5/S1 disk prolapse with attendant frequent moderate grade 3 [meaning to the level of the foot] left-sided sciatic radiation, constant moderate back pain, grade 3 muscle spasm, and occasional urinary incontinence, which is further complicated by obesity.

All the codable elements from that statement present a large number of diagnostic options. Figure 4–9 offers several coding variations, although the list is incomplete. More than 20 other codes would be acceptable. This suggests we have an extensive number of diagnoses or management options. An extensive number of codable ICD diagnoses could be justified if all of the diagnostic entities were not the direct result of the single causative tissue of disk prolapsed. (I began with the assumption that the disk prolapse was

FIGURE 4–9

Example of Coding Options

Diagnoses	Possible ICD Codes
Sciatica	729.5, 722.10
Back pain	724.2
Urinary incontinence	788.30, 788.39
Obesity	278.0, 278.0, 278.1
Disk prolapse	722.93, 722.10, 722.6, 722.70, 722.52, 722.53
Muscle spasm	847.9, 728.85, 724.8

producing the back pain and a neurologic bladder. In addition, I recognize that obesity is a separate diagnostic entity from disk disease. Obesity, by itself, has over a dozen different causative factors. I list it as a complicating factor in this example only to demonstrate how obesity complicates management options and utilization data. I do not imply it to be a result of disk disease.)

As the differential diagnosis is pared to one causative tissue, it becomes more obvious that the number of diagnoses is limited. The use of the diagnostic statement makes this clearer.

Isolating to the causative tissue or organ system reduces the choices to a root number of diagnostic options. Likewise, management options become clearer as the tissue is more closely identified. In this case, I would have chosen the diagnosis for disk prolapse (722.10). The decision to use a limited number of diagnoses is more in keeping with the system design. The remaining codable elements (i.e., urinary incontinence, obesity, sciatica, back pain, and muscle spasm) are viewed as complicating and attendant factors.

The best way to add internal consistency is to decide what number of diagnoses constitutes minimal, limited, moderate, and extensive consistent with your own coding decisions. The construction of a chart is very helpful in deciding borderline cases and facilitates more rapid coding.

As presented in Figure 4–10, I suggest that one is the *minimal* number of diagnoses. (Remember health is a diagnosis, but not codable.) In my scheme, the *limited* number of diagnoses—that is, the number of causative tissues or organ systems that have produced symptoms—is one to two; *multiple* suggests two, and *exten-*

FIGURE 4–10

Number of Diagnoses or Management Options

Minimal	=	1
Limited	=	1–2
Multiple	=	2
Extensive	=	3 or more

sive suggests three or more. Others may disagree; but as long as their reasoning is substantiated, the resultant data chart will make data collection and decision making more consistent.

Amount and/or Complexity of Data to Be Reviewed

As with the number of diagnoses or management options, there is no written formula as to what constitutes a specific amount of data. It seems logical that the amount and/or complexity of data to be reviewed would be whatever is needed to support the differential diagnosis and the diagnoses made and management options considered. Keeping with our simple orthopedic example, my in-office committee suggested a limited amount of data could be as simple as a plain film lumbar radiographic series.

A moderate amount could be plain film, MRI, possibly a CT, other outside records, and electrodiagnostic studies. An extensive amount could possibly contain other materials, including retests and multiple outside records.

With the addition of decisions I've made on the number of diagnoses or management options and the amount and/or complexity of data to be reviewed for the orthopedic example, the choice chart introduced earlier in Figure 4–8 becomes more informative, as shown in Figure 4–11. In fact, the chart is nearly complete. All that remains to be able to consistently make appropriate level decisions is to complete the section on risk of complications and/or morbidity or mortality.

Risk of Complications and/or Morbidity or Mortality

We'll refer again to the diagnostic statement about the orthopedic case given previously. I have added a complicating factor to change the level of suspicion of morbidity and mortality. Notice

FIGURE 4–11

Medical Decision Making Code Level Choice Chart

Number of Diagnoses or Management Options	Amount and/or Complexity of Data to Be Reviewed	Risk of Complications and/or Morbidity or Mortality	Type of Decision Making
Minimal 1	Minimal or none	Minimal	Straightforward
Limited 1–2	Limited Plain film series Hx* and Ex**	Low	Low complexity
Multiple 2	Moderate Plain film series + CT, MRI, outside records, and electrodiagnostic studies Hx and Ex	Moderate	Moderate complexity
Extensive 3 or more	Extensive Anything in excess of that used for moderate	Extensive	High complexity

* Hx = history
** Ex = examination

how it can affect the number of diagnostic options and decision levels.

The patient is suffering from a trauma-induced left-lateral L5/S1 disk prolapse with attendant frequent moderate grade 3 [meaning to the level of the foot] left-sided sciatic radiation, constant moderate back pain, grade 3 muscle spasm, and occasional urinary incontinence, which is complicated by obesity, prostatic hypertrophy, and diabetes.

Clearly, the diagnostic options have become more confused. The inclusion of involvement of the prostate raises the question in the physician's mind of prostatic cancer, thus raising the risk of complications and/or morbidity or mortality. Although trauma is a prime consideration for etiology of pain and muscle spasm, the suspicion of cancer in certain age groups is always present. With the finding of prostatic hypertrophy the physician must consider the possibility of cancer as an alternative cause for the sciatica, back pain, and muscle spasm. Additionally, is the urinary difficulty neurological or the result of some other process? To decide which is the true causative tissue or organ system of the complaints, the physician must perform other diagnostic procedures. This brings us to the most influential of all of the factors of medical decision making: the risk of complication and/or morbidity or mortality.

To choose the correct level of risk, it helps to keep in mind the differential diagnosis of the patient. If we view risk of complications and/or morbidity or mortality as a differential diagnosis, our choice becomes much easier. In our simple orthopedic example, this risk differential conveniently falls into distinctive age groups: 0–26, 27–40, and over 40.

In the 0–26 age group, the majority of patients' complaints will be a result of congenital or developmental conditions, primary osteopathology, and trauma. In the second orthopedic group, 27–40, complaints result mostly from trauma, with congenital abnormalities tending to be a complicating factor rather than a primary causative diagnostic entity.

In the third age group, over 40, we see a differential automatically consisting of metastatic carcinoma, multiple myeloma, systemic illness, arthritides, cardiovascular disease, and trauma. As a result, the level of risk of complications and/or morbidity or mortality is higher in the extremes of the patient age pool than in the middle. These extreme age groups automatically dictate higher E/M code choices and offer more root diagnostic options, and increase the levels of morbidity and mortality. Thus, these age groups to tend to have a higher utilization cost associated with them. Data collection that fails to account for age will not account for a large variance in utilization, making statistical predictions unreliable.

Other subdivisions of the patient population are appropriate for particular situations. The age groups I picked are rather large; some people recommend that smaller age groups be used. I suggest that in constructing your database you pick groups that will easily represent your patient populations and not make data analysis too difficult.

Additional laboratory or ultrasound will need to be performed on the patient to ascertain the health or involvement of the prostate. But these procedures come after the examination and management decisions are made. Thus, the key in determining the correct level of risk is a differential diagnosis decision rather than the performance of diagnostic tests. This differential diagnosis would most appropriately be done by a physician or other trained professional. Finally, clear communication of this decision will ensure that the coder enters the correct code on the claim form.

PROCEDURE FOR SELECTION OF CORRECT CODE LEVEL

After the construction of the choice chart, it should be relatively easy to select the correct levels of medical decision making. The different levels of history, examination, and medical decision making combine to allow various code choices, as shown in Figure 4–12. But correct code choices depend on correct level decisions for all three components. The correct levels of history and examination will have already been met by fulfilling the requirements outlined in Figures 4–3 and 4–7. In new-patient situations, all three of the key components (history, examination, and medical decision making) must be met or exceeded to justify a code choice. In es-

FIGURE 4–12

Factors in Determination of Code Choices

History +	Examination +	Medical Decision = Making	Code Choices
Problem focused	Problem focused	Straightforward	
Expanded problem focused	Expanded problem focused	Low complexity	?
Detailed	Detailed	Moderate complexity	
Comprehensive	Comprehensive	High complexity	

F I G U R E 4–13

Example of Levels Required to Justify Specific Codes

History +	Examination +	Medical Decision = Making	Code Choices
Problem focused	Problem focused	Straightforward	99201
Expanded problem focused	Expanded problem focused	Straightforward	99202
Detailed	Detailed	Low complexity	99203
Comprehensive	Comprehensive	Moderate complexity	99204
Comprehensive	Comprehensive	High complexity	99205

tablished or follow-up situations, only two of the three key components need to be met.

Figure 4–13 lists the examination, history, and medical decision levels needed to justify codes 99201, 99202, 99203, 99204, and 99205, which appear in the CPT code book. Note that a detailed history, detailed examination, and low complexity justifies a 99203 code choice. A problem-focused history, problem-focused examination, and straightforward decision making justifies a 99201 code choice. But what happens when you have mixed levels of key components, such as comprehensive history, detailed examination, and low complexity of medical decision making? The system becomes a bit confused. This is where the addition of a few numbers to your charts can help dramatically, as the following discussion will demonstrate.

An Easier Way of E/M Coding

In the past, coders had to memorize or continually look at the constituent parts of an E/M code selection. But the linear format of the choice chart allows users to easily assign values to each level and subdivision involved and determine codes without memorizing the constituent parts of a particular E/M code. I have done this in Figure 4–14. The sum of values assigned to each component will

FIGURE 4–14

Example of Choice Chart that Includes Level Values

Number of Diagnoses or Management Options	Amount and/or Complexity of Data to Be Reviewed	Risk of Complications and/or Morbidity or Mortality	Type of Decision Making
Minimal	Minimal or none	Minimal	Straightforward
1			
(3)	(6)	(9)	(18–35)
Limited	Limited	Low	Low complexity
1–2	Plain film series Hx and Ex		
(12)	(15)	(18)	(36–71)
Multiple	Moderate	Moderate	Moderate complexity
2	Plain film series + CT, MRI, outside records, and electrodiagnostic studies Hx and Ex		
(21)	(24)	(27)	(72–81)
Extensive	Extensive	Extensive	High complexity
3 or more	Anything in excess of that used for moderate		
(30)	(33)	(36)	(82–99)

automatically correspond to the correct code. First, determine the level of medical decision making, then move to the code finder, shown in Figure 4–15. The same can be done with all other E/M codes. (These have already been done and can be obtained through a service. Contact the author for the address.)

To explain the process, I wish to return to my simple orthopedic example. I find that the patient is a 48-year-old man. He is a new patient to our outpatient facility (or we haven't seen him in

FIGURE 4–15

Code Finder

History +	Examination +	Medical Decision Making =	Code Choices
Problem focused (3)	Problem focused (6)	Straightforward (9)	99201 (18–27)
Expanded problem focused (12)	Expanded problem focused (15)	Low complexity (18)	99202 (28–36)
			99203 (37–63)
Detailed (21)	Detailed (24)	Moderate complexity (27)	99204 (64–89)
Comprehensive (30)	Comprehensive (33)	High complexity (36)	99205 (90–99)

three years), which means our coding choices are 99201, 99202, 99203, 99204, and 99205 (see Figure 4–15). The patient has been seen by the physician, who rendered the following diagnostic statement:

> The patient is suffering from a trauma-induced left-lateral L5/S1 disk prolapse with attendant frequent moderate grade 3 [meaning to the level of the foot] left-sided sciatic radiation, constant moderate back pain, grade 3 muscle spasm, and occasional urinary incontinence, which is complicated by obesity, prostatic hypertrophy, and diabetes.

(Remember, the prostatic hypertrophy and diabetes are complicating factors, but specifically they are co-morbid processes. They are independent of the disk condition and have their own courses and are managed separately.)

In addition, the physician has provided us with the level of risk of complications and/or morbidity or mortality, which is moderate in this case. Together with the patient's file, we can code accurately every time.

First, the causative tissues or organ systems are coded by ICD number. The number of diagnoses are identified on the choice chart. I circle sections for identification on my charts, but they are shown as shaded in Figure 4–16.

Second, the level of risk of complications and / or morbidity or mortality is identified, also shaded in Figure 4–16. (Remember, it must be provided by the physician or care provider.)

FIGURE 4–16

Example of Choice Chart with Specific Values Identified

Number of Diagnoses or Management Options	Amount and/or Complexity of Data to Be Reviewed	Risk of Complications and/or Morbidity or Mortality	Type of Decision Making
Minimal 1 (3)	Minimal or none (6)	Minimal (9)	Straightforward (18–35)
Limited 1–2 (12)	Limited Plain film series Hx* and Ex** (15)	Low (18)	Low complexity (36–71)
Multiple 2 (21)	Moderate Plain film series + CT, MRI, outside records, and electrodiagnostic studies Hx and Ex (24)	Moderate (27)	Moderate complexity (72–81)
Extensive 3 or more (30)	Extensive Anything in excess of that used for moderate (33)	Extensive (36)	High complexity (82–99)

* Hx = history

** Ex = examination

Third, the studies, outside records, history, and exam information are evaluated. This patient's file shows a plain film study, electrodiagnostic studies, and a serological laboratory study. Through the chart we have constructed, we have determined this is a moderate amount of data to be reviewed (shaded in Figure 4–16). We then sum the values for a limited amount of diagnosis, a moderate amount of data, and a moderate risk (12, 24, and 27, respectively). They total 63, which would place the type of decision making at the low complexity level.

Fourth, use the code finder chart in Figure 4–17 to determine the level of the three key components for correct code selection. A moderate level of decision making has been determined. The physician could supply the level of history and examination, but a quick review of the patient's file will provide the same information.

Fifth, identify the key component levels, shaded in Figure 4–17. In this case, a detailed history was obtained and an expanded problem focused examination was performed. The numbers total 63, indicating that a 99203 code is appropriate.

FIGURE 4–17

Code Finder with Specific Values Identified

History +	Examination +	Medical Decision Making =	Code Choices
Problem focused (3)	Problem focused (6)	Straightforward (9)	99201 (18–27)
Expanded problem focused (12)	Expanded problem focused (15)	Low complexity (18)	99202 (28–36)
			99203 (37–63)
Detailed (21)	Detailed (24)	Moderate complexity (27)	99204 (64–89)
Comprehensive (30)	Comprehensive (33)	High complexity (36)	99205 (90–99)

Final Words on E/M Coding

As you can see, the complexity of the E/M coding process is what has caused many facilities to cross-walk from old fee schedules. The physician is the key to correct coding. It is her or his work that is being coded; ultimately, it is her or his responsibility. The construction of the medical decision making and the code finder charts should be made in committee. This committee work is educational to staffs and will also serve as a basis for Total Quality Management/Continuous Quality Improvement. This same information will also later become the basis for outcome studies and clinical variation studies. Physicians can greatly speed up administrative work and improve data accuracy by providing the level of risk of complications and/or morbidity or mortality, the level of history, and the level of examination.

In the indemnity-based insurance system, a common reason for denial or delay of reimbursement is that the level of examination is not justified by the diagnosis given. Training staffs in diagnostic structuring and proper E/M coding will alleviate this problem. Since the majority of business in most offices still comes from indemnity insurance plans, it is certainly worthwhile for those staffs to learn correct coding.

5

C H A P T E R

Utilization Measurements

While I was studying for my masters in healthcare administration at Loma Linda University, the department chairman, Dr. Thompson, who earned his doctorate in accounting, made a remark that captures the essence of managed care: "Managed care is how an accountant would practice medicine." With outcome studies, clinical variations studies, capitated contracting, and length of stay and utilization predictions, we can see how accurate Dr. Thompson's remark is.

In the indemnity-based insurance dynamic, the insurance carrier has the most control but also the greatest financial risk. To control risk, the carrier has to control utilization, that is, how much of its products (the supply of medical services) the consumer can use. The more the carrier can limit services, the more profit it makes. This may be hard for the public to accept, but it should be expected in a capitalistic medical delivery system. Utilization control is the single biggest factor that affects profits.

To adequately control utilization it has to be measurable. The measurement tool then becomes the basis for utilization prediction. Thus, statistics and accounting have become even more important in the healthcare industry. Earlier in this book, I stated that insurance companies have failed to accurately predict long-term utilization because of variations contained within diagnostic and related groupings. The upstream diversification and gatekeeper concepts, which were hallmarks of the HMO and managed care delivery system, worked for a time; but as the legal liability of denying care under the pretense of utilization control rises, profit margins shrink. As insurance companies fail to maintain profit margins, they abandon utilization control techniques and adopt broader, more comprehensive changes in the healthcare delivery and financing system.

These comprehensive changes have altered the relationships between carrier, provider, and consumer. One of the latest changes in healthcare delivery is the emergence of fully capitated care. In this system, the provider takes on the risk associated with utilization control rather than the carrier. However, utilization control remains the key to achieving profits, but now for the provider.

To effectively control utilization, providers must measure it. Insurance carriers have traditionally measured utilization by determining the average length of stay (LOS) associated with a diagnosis. Carriers limit utilization and thus treatment length and cost associated with it to providers on the basis of the length of stay measurement. Physicians and staffs have often had to argue that the determined length of stay for a given diagnosis is insufficient to treat patients. In an indemnity-based insurance system it would, of course, be to the provider's advantage to argue this position. The insurance carrier obviously argues the opposite. This puts the consumer in the middle, wondering who is telling the truth. This controversy is fueled by stories of insurance carriers denying care or of money-hungry doctors keeping patients in care longer than insurance carriers deem necessary.

The bare truth is all parties want the most money or services possible. Insurance companies and doctors want the most profit they can achieve. Consumers want the best, cheapest, and most healthcare for their money. I have yet to find a consumer who purchased an insurance policy without expecting to get more out of it than she or he paid in premiums.

Thus, we are left with the problem of providing healthcare while controlling utilization in a market dynamic of conflicting interests. A balance is theoretically possible. A mathematical model could be constructed to predict utilization even if every consumer were to demand and receive every treatment or diagnostic test desired. And a healthcare system based on that model could be constructed. It would just be too expensive for anyone to afford. In a capitalistic system, a balance must be found in which a reasonable amount of services are rendered for a reasonable profit. Any out-of-balance relationship will cause the system to break down in an attempt to find equilibrium.

Doctors in an indemnity-based system are motivated to increase profits by artificially raising referrals or prolonging care, which artificially raises utilization. In reaction, insurance companies try to control utilization via a variety of means discussed earlier in this book. However, the public contributes to this problem by not maintaining responsibility for what is charged to the insurance carrier and by filing ever-increasing numbers of malpractice suits against providers. If utilization is to decrease, consumers must have reasonable expectations about the healthcare services they receive. They must learn to expect only what is medically necessary to cure or relieve them of their medical problems. They must also try to maintain healthier lifestyles.

What is obvious is that a balance must be found. Doctors in a managed care or capitated environment must educate the public. And they must control utilization to survive. For the physician or insurance carrier to be able to control utilization effectively, it must be measured accurately. To date this has not been done.

MEASURING UTILIZATION

A commonly used measurement of utilization is based on length of stay data collected from HCFA 1500 and UB82 claim forms. The measurement follows the logic that a given diagnosis calls for a specific treatment plan, which in most cases leads to a consistent result. This may seem simple enough, but problems exist. First, as suggested in the previous chapter, variation in the diagnosis produces variation in the data captured. Second, the procedures used for a particular patient may vary from those typically used because of complicating factors that preclude certain treatment choices. Third, not all patient results or responses to a given treatment are the same. Fourth, the information is collected from a biased sample, namely, an indemnity-driven data pool. Fifth, the data bias continues with the commingling of indemnity data with managed care data. Sixth, insurance companies may manipulate data to reflect a lower average length of stay than one might typically expect.

The first four points have been previously discussed. The fifth and sixth need to be explored.

Patient, Provider, and Carrier Self-Interest

It is an economic truth that all of the parties involved in healthcare work in their own best interest. This is how a capitalistic system works. It reflects the checks and balances of supply and demand. A patient will buy a policy expecting to use more than she or he expects to pay.

A physician will tend to supply services as long as no harm comes to the patient. This tendency was noticed by Roemer in his study of hospital vacancy rates and slow admission times. His study showed that as beds became empty, more referrals occurred and longer stays resulted. Some cynical observers suggested that this was from pressure of administrators. Others dispute the study out of hand.

Insurance carriers work in their best interest by controlling costs and determining the most beneficial premium rate for them. Additionally, it is my contention that some insurance carriers and claims review companies purposely manipulates data to misrepresent actual LOS and average fees associated with procedures. This manipulation of fees is easy to spot in claims reviews, as any medical manager or administrator can attest. For example, I have noticed in the Southern California area two new games currently being played with fees associated with outpatient physical therapy.

The first game is for a company to review fees for outpatient physical therapy using the worker's compensation fee schedule rather than actual outpatient or typical fees. This tends to reduce fees an average of 30 to 50 percent. The second part of this game is that the review company, which we are supposed to believe is independent, will not tell the provider if a fee is too low by its study, only if it is too high.

The second new game involves a new computer system that many carriers are purchasing. This computer system has data from several contributing carriers. This data are then used as a basis for determining LOS and fees for zip-code-specific areas. I have several problems with its approach. First, the insurance contract states that it will pay for reasonable costs associated with necessary medical care to cure or relieve the effects of accident or illness. But reasonable is never defined. Carriers using this computer system contend that a reasonable fee falls within the 80th percentile of the average fee charges (discussed later in this chapter). The problem is the computer system contains managed care data (fees and LOS), which are not usual or customary. Managed care data are special in that LOS is often determined by someone other than the provider (hence managed), and fees are often reduced in consideration for an increased volume. I have not been able to confirm it as of the printing of this book, but I would not be surprised if this computer system also contained worker's compensation data, which would also lower fee averages.

The inclusion of data from several insurance carriers is intriguing from a legal point of view. I asked a lawyer if the insurance carriers that were combining data were in effect attempting to control another business by fixing fees. If so, this would seem to be a violation of antitrust. He agrees and is currently building a file on denials and review procedures.

On the basis of my observations of the review process and the expected behavior of competing individuals in a capitalistic system, I contend that insurance carriers manipulate statistics to gain advantage over the provider and the consumer. As such, all statistics offered by a carrier in a managed care or capitated contract are highly suspect, if not totally unbelievable.

Determining ALOS

I wish to explore, once again, the simple diagnosis of sprain and how the diagnosis and the ICD code associated with it can form an inaccurate basis for determining LOS.

The majority of sprains are the common grade one and mildly moderate grade two. These low-grade sprains typically require little or no professional treatment and take a couple of weeks to heal. For example, the common grade one ankle sprain is characterized by swelling, joint stability, and minor pain. Most individuals wouldn't seek professional treatment and would instead apply a correct home remedy of rest, ice, compression, and elevation. However, in the indemnity-based system, many insured patients tend to use medical resources for a simple sprain; likewise, some of their doctors will treat that sprain with unnecessary medical procedures. This results in insurance company computers containing a tremendous amount of claim data representing mild and lower-grade moderate sprain, which cannot be differentiated from more severe degrees of sprain.

It has been suggested that mild sprains involve tears of approximately 30 percent or less of the ligament. Severe sprains are classified as a total rupture of the supportive ligament. These injuries are not as common as mild or moderate sprains. This type of ligament rupture will need surgical intervention and may take several months to heal. Moderate sprains fall between mild and severe; they are characterized as having between 31 and 99 percent of the ligament torn. The key differential between these three degrees of sprain is the amount of joint stability. Moderate injuries may take a couple of weeks to several months to heal.

The same ICD code is used for all three types of sprain, but the course and cost of treatment for each may be radically different, varying from an elastic bandage to a cast or even surgery. This simple example should show that variation in the severity of illness represents a huge problem in predicting utilization.

Many providers combat the limitations carriers place on care by using a code that indicates a more severe condition than actually exists. But remember, the problem of variation in severity of illness exists for every diagnosis and diagnostic code. Additionally, this code inflation corrupts in-office data. Since an insurance carrier cannot determine the severity of illness by the ICD code reported on the HCFA 1500 claim form, it must request extra information from the provider or deny the claim outright as being made outside a reasonable time frame.

The need to provide extra information would open the door for the physician to justify additional treatment that may or may not actually be needed. However, since it assumes that the physician is working in self-interest, the insurance carrier will likely make it difficult for him or her to extend treatment unnecessarily. Also, the eventual processing of additional information would be time consuming and costly for the carrier. As a result, the carrier would likely deny the claim as being unnecessary on the basis of its study of the same or similar claims submitted.

The carrier could justify this denial of care with the data collected on HCFA claim forms. The data on lesser-degree injuries will outnumber that for severe injuries. Thus, the average length of care as determined from the data would be less than typically required for more complex cases; that is, the extreme number of patients with lower-grade sprains included in the data pool causes an artificial downward shift in LOS. These patients cannot be eliminated from data pool since there is no way to identify these claims, as the diagnosis does not specify severity of illness. Unless the data pool is adjusted to account for differences in severity, the average LOS will not necessarily reflect real needs.

Assume there are 14 sprain claims in the insurance carrier's computer, 8 are the lesser grade one and mildly moderate grade two sprains, 3 are moderate, 2 are moderately severe, and 1 is severe. The typical response time for each of the sprain categories is 1–2 weeks for mild sprains, 3–5 weeks for moderate, 6–8 weeks for moderately severe sprains, and 9–12 weeks for severe. How, then, does the carrier calculate an LOS?

First, consideration needs to be given to what is meant by *average*. Average can be calculated three ways: as mode, median, or mean. All three are measurements of central tendency and represent average.

Mode is defined as the score that appears the most often. In the case of the 14 sprains, the treatment schedule used most often would be 1–2 weeks since there are more grade one and grade two sprains than others.

Median is defined as the middle score in a series. This is what most people think of when the word *average* is used. Unfortunately, median cannot be used for categorical data, which we are discussing here.

Mean is another measure of central tendency, but it has an advantage over the others in that it can be manipulated algebraically; thus, carriers typical use it to determine ALOS. It is calculated by the sum of all the scores divided by the number of scores. As Figure 5–1 shows, the mean for the categories of mild, moderate, and severe in our example is 3.554 weeks of treatment time. This is fine for lower-grade sprains, but the upper grades require more time.

To be practical, an LOS allowance should be a range of response times rather than a specific time. This is where another statistical measurement tool comes into play. It is called the *80th percentile*. As applied to length of stay, it is defined as a period that is longer or equal to 80 percent of the other measured times. For the sprain example, the 80th percentile would be six weeks of care and the mean response time is about three and a half weeks. One would assume, then, that the insurance carrier would authorize a six-week treatment course, as average time would be somewhere between three and a half to six weeks.

This is where another statistical measurement tool is used. It is called an *outlier*. Outliers are numbers that lie beyond the range of reasonable expectation. The response time for the severe sprain appears to be an outlier, being almost twice that of the next high-

FIGURE 5-1

Mean Calculation for 14 Varying Grades of Sprain

Type	Number	Response Time
Mild, grade one	8	1–2 weeks
Moderate, grade two	3	3–5 weeks
Severely moderate, grade two +	2	6–8 weeks
Severe, grade three	1	9–12 weeks
Total	14	

$$\text{Mean grade} = \frac{\text{Sum of grades}}{\text{Number of grades}}$$

$$= \frac{(1 + 1 + 2 + 2 + 2 + 1 + 1.5 + 1.75) + (3 + 4 + 5) + (6 + 8) + 11.5}{14}$$

Mean LOS = Treatment time of 3.554 weeks

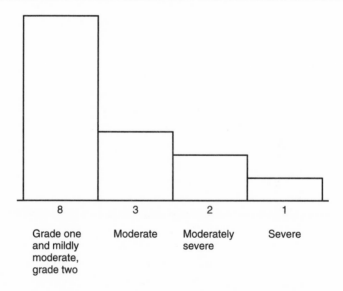

8	3	2	1
Grade one and mildly moderate, grade two	Moderate	Moderately severe	Severe

est response time. Eliminating this outlier decreases the LOS as determined by the mean and 80th percentile measures. Thus, depending on averaging methods, outliers, and other statistical methods, LOS can be a very deceiving or arbitrary number.

Providers also manipulate LOS and utilization data. Take for example the diagnosis of chest pain. This diagnosis will justify a hospital LOS of two days with almost all insurance companies, a time that is thought sufficient to determine the etiology of the chest pain and to find out if it is life threatening. However, no one can tell how long it will take to fix the cause of the pain. But knowing that the diagnosis will guarantee a minimum LOS of two days, some less-than-ethical facilities might falsely diagnose chest pain in patients to fill beds in periods of slow admissions.

In a study published in the 1950s, Milton Roemer concluded that supply (empty beds) created demand (filling those beds). This became known as Roemer's law. The law is still controversial; but after 20 years of experience in a provider-driven market, I'm more willing to believe Roemer was right than wrong.

MANAGING UTILIZATION

The healthcare market has become more competitive as a result of the increasing number of physicians and diminishing patient pools, which has led to smaller profit margins in practices. But an even greater threat to reaching profitability exists. That threat is the downward push of managing risk. Since insurance companies have failed to manage risk because of data that were insufficient to allow adequate predictability, they have adopted a brilliant strategy of pushing the risk of predicting and controlling utilization down to the providers.

A system of managed care allows carriers to protect themselves from financial loss by placing the risk involved in data and utilization decisions onto the physician. In a managed care system, the carrier pays the physician a fixed fee per patient per month (PMPM) to provide all of the care needed by that patient pool within the scope of that physician's services. A question then arises: If insurance companies failed at accurately predicting utilization and providing healthcare to a population in a market with growing demands and rapidly rising prices, how can physicians expect to succeed?

In this capitated environment, insurance carriers, armed with mountains of actuarial studies, approach physicians with contract offers, quoting statistics that are alleged to accurately predict utilization. Physicians must learn a new way of doing business in a new marketplace; that is, to achieve profitability they must reduce operating costs while facing greater administrative demands from carriers and greater patient demands for expensive technology and extreme procedures.

Indemnity-based health insurance was based on the idea of predictable mathematical models of disease. The problem is, as I've argued throughout, insurance companies collect improper and inaccurate data. They depend on incidence data to predict duration of illness and thus determine LOS, an impossible task. In addition, insurance carriers depend on providers who have an opposing interest in an indemnity-based system. These providers are not interested in controlling utilization nor in providing accurate information if it can be avoided. Thus, the data on which carriers base utilization predictions can be distorted. This hinders the carrier's ability to track variation in and assess effectiveness of policies. Diagnostic coding—the system's data driver—does not reflect variation in treatment times because it does not account for severity of illness, complicating factors, and co-morbidities.

In capitation, physicians and other providers must assume the task of predicting and controlling utilization. The accuracy of the data presented to them by insurance carriers is suspect. Their own data are inflated and inaccurate. But providers must successfully control utilization to be profitable. This will involve calculating LOS and LOS variations on an individual basis, an impossibility with the current inaccurate and uncoordinated data. Fortunately, every problem has an answer and presents even greater opportunity. Never at any other time have so many resources existed to help physicians achieve success.

I would suggest that physicians start by joining two very fine organizations. They are the Medical Group Management Association (MGMA) in Englewood, Colorado, which maintains an extensive resource library, and the Healthcare Financial Management Association (HFMA), which is tremendously helpful in understanding the financial side of medical practices. In my opinion, a physician cannot compete in today's market without the information and resources these organizations provide.

Another source of information is the publisher of this text, Irwin Professional Publishing of Burr Ridge, Illinois, which has produced many books that contain invaluable insights on issues discussed here. Two worth purchasing are *Capitation, New Oppor-*

tunities in Healthcare Delivery, by David Samuels, and *The Capitation and Risk Sharing Guidebook,* by Allison Cherney. An additional excellent source of information is the seminar series offered by Business Network, which Irwin has recently acquired. Finally, I also suggest reading basic texts in statistics and managerial accounting to enhance your ability to understand the basis of managed care.

6

CHAPTER

Performance Measurements

Chapter 5 dealt with the basic measurement of average length of stay as it applies to predicting utilization and the problems resulting from inaccurate data. In this chapter, I shall discuss how socioeconomic factors (SEFs) and complicating factors, severity of illness, and co-morbidities (CSCs) affect outcome and clinical variation studies.

OUTCOME AND CLINICAL VARIATION STUDIES

Outcome and clinical variation studies are undertaken to assess the consistency, pathways, cost, and quality of some portion of the medical treatment process. They are performance measurements based on Dr. E. Deming's work on quality concepts. Deming was a visionary who claimed that quality depended on the amount of variation in processes. His approach calls for the identification of variation in a process by measuring statistical deviation from the norm. Simply summarized, Deming's approach involves defining process, measuring outcomes and other performance variables, and determining variation. According to Deming, removing variation increases quality.

Outcome and clinical variation studies are used in the medical industry to measure process, define procedure and cost pathways, control costs, and ensure consistent quality. Although they are related, outcome and clinical variation studies examine two different parts of the medical treatment process. I would like to begin this discussion of these studies by first defining the treatment process they both measure.

Treatment Process

As discussed in previous chapters, utilization measurements are driven and determined by diagnoses. An example of this would be average LOS measurements. But performance measurements are also affected to a great degree by the treatment process.

Examine Figure 6–1. It illustrates several concepts in the medical treatment process including the basis for clinical and outcome studies. This diagram of the diagnosis-treatment-outcome process is based on several assumptions. The first is that the

FIGURE 6-1

SEF Outcome and Clinical Pathways

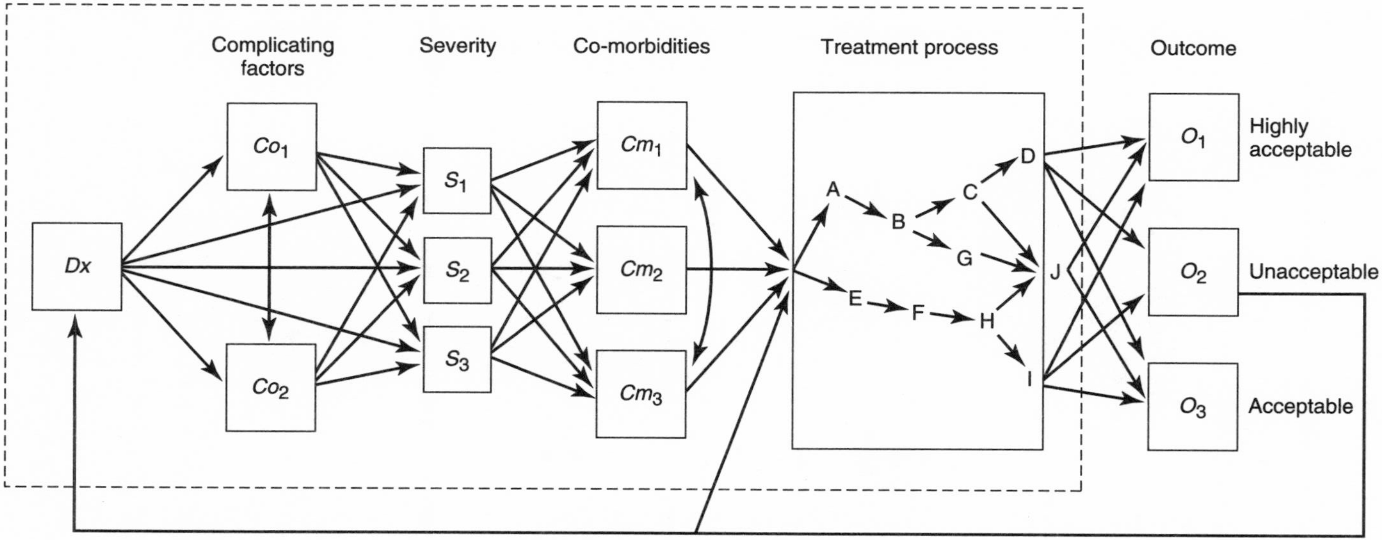

diagnosis is already established. Second, only two complicating factors exist and the patient being treated may have one or both of these factors. Third, only three degrees of severity and three co-morbid processes exist. Additionally, socioeconomic factors act as a filter that may affect treatment choices, CSCs, and even the diagnosis.

(The effect of socioeconomic factors on diagnosis is evidenced by the fact that certain ages, races, and sexes can have a disease whereas different ages, races, and sexes can't. Examples include uterine cancer, sickle cell anemia, and senile dementia. However, socioeconomic factors most likely won't have as great of an effect on severity of illness as other elements.)

The treatment process also has variation within it and is a four-step process with only three possible outcomes: highly acceptable, acceptable, and unacceptable. The choices made within this diagram outline a treatment pathway; and associating dollars with the various steps within the treatment process defines cost pathways.

The primary objective of outcome studies is to find a repeatable procedure protocol that will consistently lead to outcomes of acceptable quality. A secondary objective is to produce a predictable cost pathway. Identification of a treatment process that can yield a predictable and acceptable outcome, at a known price, will greatly aid in predicting total utilization costs.

Clinical variation is a similar measurement. It deals with procedural variations that result from physician choices. Measurement of clinical variation follows the same logic as outcome measurement. Both measurements assume that for given a diagnosis, a physician controls resource allocations via procedure choices, which in turn determines costs. With clear assessments of costs for various procedures, a provider can consistently choose a treatment that will lead to an acceptable outcome at the lowest cost.

There is truth in that assumption, but as currently used, enough problems exist with CSC and SEF assessment as to lessen the accuracy, and thus the predictability, of these measurement tools. But in fairness, these tools offer better predictability than those they replaced, which was nothing.

Provider-Driven Outcome and Variation Studies

In reality, more CSCs and SEFs exist than Figure 6–1 illustrates. Additionally, treatment choices may be more simple or complex than outlined in the figure. Caregivers must determine known and suspected factors to accurately collect data. Then a process chart must be generated for each of the diagnoses given to accurately measure clinical variation and outcomes. This sounds like a tremendous undertaking; but most specialties use a limited number of diagnoses and procedures. What will also help in the construction of this process chart is the consistent use of a structured diagnosis, as discussed in Chapter 3.

Lovelace Health System in New Mexico undertook such an effort. Using data on costs, key procedures, and outcomes of care, Lovelace developed a model called Episodes of Care (EOC). Several diagnostic conditions were selected for EOC projects. Ultimately, Lovelace developed one-page practice guidelines for providers. Thus, provider-driven outcome studies can define protocols and costs.

For the typical medical office, in-office data collection is based on file reviews of previously treated patients. CSC and SEF data is collected through surveys of staff and caregivers. All of this information is used to create a process chart.

Patterns of relationships between CSCs, SEFs, treatment choices, and costs become immediately evident. Referring again to Figure 6–1, imagine that the treatment pathway for the patient population follows the path A–B–C–D 40 percent of the time and A–B–G–J 60 percent of the time, and both result in outcome O_1, highly acceptable.

The comparison of these two pathways, assuming that the same CSCs and SEFs are present, is a clinical variation study. That is, the acceptability, cost, and risk involved with the selection of the C–D would be compared to those for the G–J components. The outcomes of different pathways in a clinical variation study are the same, in this example, highly acceptable. The focus of the study, then, is on the determinants of that outcome.

A comparison made between pathways, for example, A–B–C–D and E–F–H–I, that had different results is an outcome study. The objective of such a comparison is to achieve a consistent level of quality. As is easily seen, clinical variation and outcome studies are closely related but actually measure different parts of the process. For example, if the O_1 and O_3 outcomes are favorable but the pathway reaching O_1 is cost-prohibitive, a clinical variation study will dictate using the pathway to O_3 when cost is a concern. If the outcomes are the same, clinical variation studies will outline differences in acceptability, cost, and risk of various pathways.

Administrative and claims-based data are limited in the amount of clinical detail they provide. Sophisticated models and methods of risk adjustment do exist. In my opinion, IE220NI has been chief among researchers advocating more sophisticated risk adjustments. But again, hospital data do not relay as much information as needed. Inaccuracies in coding offer further problems when the number of diagnostic fields is restricted. Researchers have found that expanding the number of data fields increased reports of co-morbidity; results were similar among patients who had died and those who had survived. It is apparent that the data relayed to insurance carriers do not contain enough detail for accurate outcome or clinical variation studies, and as such, providers should not readily accept insurance carriers' actuarial data for performance prediction.

Assignment of CSC, SEF, dollars, and treatment descriptions to the process chart in Figure 6–1 produces the process chart shown in Figure 6–2. Using the diagnostically structured statement developed in earlier chapters, I can generate a treatment pathway for the individual patient. When analyzed, the treatment pathway is adjusted by the CSC grouping $Co_1-Co_2-S_2-Cm_1$, and viewed within the SEF context. The treatment pathway could be any of several different paths, some of which lead to the same outcome. For the sake of discussion, assume the treatment pathway, costs, and outcome for 100 patients as shown in Figure 6–3.

Given 100 patients with the same diagnosis and the same SEFs and CSCs, we can meaningfully compare the clinical variations and outcomes. Figure 6–3 shows that the 40 patients of the A–B–C–D treatment path can be compared with the 40 patients of the A–B–G–J treatment path. Of the 40 patient in the A–B–C–D

FIGURE 6-2

Process Chart for White Males, 40 Years Old, Height–Weight Disproportionate, Labor-Intensive Occupation

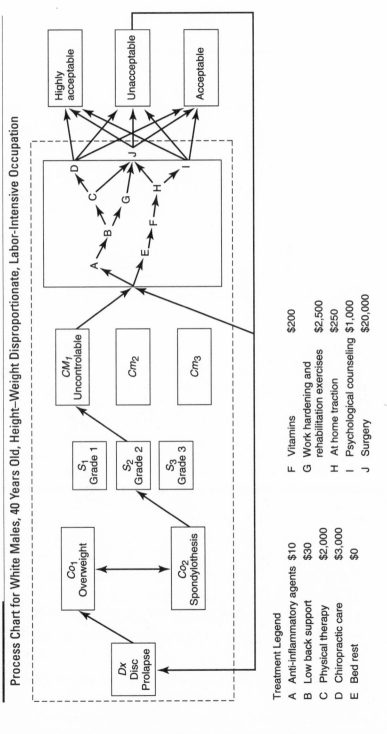

Treatment Legend

A Anti-inflammatory agents $10
B Low back support $30
C Physical therapy $2,000
D Chiropractic care $3,000
E Bed rest $0

F Vitamins $200
G Work hardening and
   rehabilitation exercises $2,500
H At home traction $250
I Psychological counseling $1,000
J Surgery $20,000

FIGURE 6–3

Sample Clinical Variation and Outcome Cost Study

Treatment Pathway	Number of Patients	Number of Results		%	Cost
A–B–C–D	40	O_1	20	50	$ 5,040
		O^2	15	38	5,040
		O^3	5	12	5,040
A–B–G–J	40	O_1	15	38	22,540
		O_2	5	12	22,540
		O_3	20	50	22,540
E–F–H–J	15	O_1	5	33	20,450
		O_2	5	33	20,450
		O_3	5	33	20,450
E–F–H–T	5	O_1	2	40	1,450
		O_2	1	20	1,450
		O_3	2	40	1,450

path, 62 percent of the patients had acceptable to highly acceptable outcomes and 38 percent had unacceptable outcomes, with a cost of care at $5,040. The A–B–G–J pathway had a 88 percent acceptable or better outcome rate, with only a 12 percent failure rate, but at the cost of $22,540.

Since both pathways had a high success rate, both are desirable. Yet consideration must be given to the issues of acceptability of treatment, risk, and cost. When the treatment process is graphed, beneficial or troublesome areas can be isolated. New protocols for cost-effective treatments can be designed using elements of other successful pathways.

Given their assumption of risk in the current managed care market, providers will find it incumbent to have accurate data on outcomes and the factors that lead to those outcomes. Without this accurate data, a provider's ability to predict utilization is seriously compromised. As David Samuels correctly pointed out, insurance companies have successfully avoided risk. They sidestep losses.

Clinical variation and outcome studies are valuable performance tools that can be used successfully in managed care environments. These performance measurements, combined with utilization measurements adjusted by CSC and SEF data, allow physicians to accurately predict utilization.

7
CHAPTER

In-Office Data Capture

It is impossible for insurance carriers to accurately determine utilization with the data they have collected, as previously discussed. The utilization statistics an insurance carrier offers a provider are based on data submitted by thousands of providers, which is unadjusted for complicating factors, severity of illness, and co-morbidities. To protect themselves, however, the providers distort this in-office data. Obviously, since the provider and the carrier are operating from their own self-interest in a competitive environment, both sets of data will reflect their own attempts to limit or extend utilization.

In a shared risk, or capitated, environment, the carrier and the provider are no longer competitors; they are both interested in controlling utilization. This is often interpreted as denying care. Often providers and consumers alike admonish carriers for their lack of concern for the consumer. News stories and lawsuits point out shortcomings and examples of the "victims" of the healthcare crisis. There is some truth in some of these stories and justification for some lawsuits, but there are also fraudulent and unethical providers and consumers. The underlying fact is that the number of abuses, be they by providers, consumers, or carriers, is not as high as one of the other competing groups would have you believe. The competing group has an interest in maintaining that belief to justify their attempts to control actions.

All parties involved in a capitated care plan need to work to reasonably control utilization, otherwise the system will not be efficient. The utilization of a capitated population is not known. It is "experienced." This means that the efforts of the carriers, providers, and consumers will combine to produce the actual utilization characteristics. True utilization predictions of the actual resources required to provide care to a population must be made in order to establish costs.

At this time, however, the stakeholders are not fully cooperating. As competition has grown between insurance carriers, their profit margins have shrunk, forcing the need for more accurate statistical predictions. Insurance carriers don't have the information needed to make those predictions, because it was never collected. The insurance claim forms used by providers limit the amount of data collected, thus decreasing the accuracy of utilization predictions. In addition, consumers, as a group, fail to recognize the impact of their healthcare utilization practices on the ultimate costs. Those in the healthcare industry can best modify this consumer behavior by educating the public on the need to make healthy lifestyle choices and to keep reasonable expectations of outcomes.

Providers will be the ultimate controller of utilization. They also are the single best source of utilization data. Providers can generate more accurate utilization data by reviewing in-office files and reconstructing the treatment experience with a given diagnosis. However, providers must recognize that the data they are collecting also contain biases and inaccuracies. Many hospitals have attempted to measure outcomes and clinical variation and to construct clinical and cost pathways. Individual practitioners have not undertaken these studies, but they will need to in order to accept capitated care contracts.

To measure outcomes and clinical variation and to construct clinical and cost pathways, providers need to design data capture systems and understand factors that affect utilization. The remainder of this chapter is devoted to illustrating the construction of a simple system for collecting data and predicting utilization profiles.

STEPS IN COLLECTING DATA

The first step in collecting in-office data is to recognize factors besides complications, severity, and co-morbidity that affect utilization. Socioeconomic factors such as race, income, education, age, and sex also affect utilization. Information on these two groups of factors is what Iezzoni and colleagues outlined as the clinical and administrative data missing from utilization predictions.[1] Those researchers are not alone in that opinion.

In a recent article in the *MGMA Journal*, Francine Gaillour, medical director of Phamis Inc., stated that managed care "puts physicians in the insurance business."[2] She further stated that physicians must track outcomes and improve quality and population management. Population management, explained Gaillour, involves stratifying populations according to risk by clinical condition and by demographic attributes.

By now you can see that in-office data capture is essential in managed care, particularly if your office is considering at-risk contracts. Prime in importance is diagnosis. It absolutely must be adjusted for complicating factors, severity, and co-morbidities (CSCs). A meeting of the physicians and staff in your office will produce a quick list of suspected CSC factors. Those factors combined with socioeconomic factors will produce a list of elements that will give real meaning and predictability to your in-office data.

An easy way to start the process of data collection is to select a quantity of recent files. File selection should be random, with no preselection process. The exact number of files to be collected can be determined mathematically; generally, increasing the number of files increases statistical power, but let's leave that discussion for a later time. The idea is, the more the sample of files represents your patient population, the better the statistics will reflect your practice.

Divide the files into diagnostic groups. If your office has tended to use pattern diagnoses or other coding schemes, it will become readily apparent when these files are reviewed.

Ultimately, all the diagnoses applicable to the medical specialty will need to be tracked. In a managed care system, a provider would be wise to limit the diagnoses to the most common that he or she renders treatment for, expanding the diagnostic list as experience justifies. The in-office file review is the beginning of is what is known as an *actuarial study.*

Actuarial Studies

There are two primary methods of performing actuarial studies: the fee-for-service method and the budgetary or cost method. Two resources that discuss these methods are a monograph by Sutton and Sorbo entitled *Actuarial Issues in the Fee-For-Service/Prepaid Medical Group*[3] and a lecture series given by Lawrence Benson entitled *Managing Capitation and Risk.*[4] You may obtain more information about Benson's series by contacting McGraw-Hill, the publisher of this book.

Benson's material outlines the fee-for-service method. This method is acceptable, and most practitioners would probably find it easier to use than the budgetary or cost method. I feel, as do Sutton and Sorbo, that certain problems exist with the fee-for-service method. The primary problem is the method's lack of emphasis on the impact of physician and nursing staff costs, particularly since medicine is labor intensive. The budgetary or cost method is more in line with activity-based accounting methods and the use of cost centers, which is more accurate than traditional accounting methods.

However, the fee-for-service is simpler to figure and more familiar looking to most offices than the budgetary or cost method. Thus, I feel that the fee-for-service method is a good place to start for less sophisticated offices. The method that gives you the most confidence and comfort is the way to go. Keep in mind that all methods have problems; the more you understand the shortcomings of your tools, the better off you will be.

The fee-for-service method projects the cost of services based on equivalent charges. The factors considered are frequency of use and length of stay. The budgetary or cost method assesses how many full-time employees it will take to provide the necessary care for the prepaid population. The distinction is that the fee-for-service system assumes that a treatment will follow a cost pathway within certain limits, whereas the budgetary method is based on the cost of employees needed to perform or render a service. The former tends to view employees as fixed costs; the latter accounts for the variable costs of performing the services. Most offices already use traditional accounting rather than activity-based methods and cost centers (physicians and staff needed to perform a service), so they will find the fee-for-service approach to be more familiar.

The raw data you currently have in your office are driven by diagnoses. Thus, cost pathways, which are defined by procedures, are dependent variables to diagnoses. Once you have gathered data on experiential cost pathways per diagnosis, you can convert to an activity-based accounting system for budgeting. This will become important later when you need to consider how much service you can provide to satisfy a contract, or for determining which procedures you cannot cost-effectively perform. It will also help you calculate potential profit.

So, begin by pulling a few hundred files. The diagnoses in these files should be in the standard diagnostic structure as outlined in Chapter 3. This can be done by a physician or a physician's assistant. It is important to avoid general diagnoses. The closer the file specifies causative tissue or diagnostic entities, the better it will be when it comes to calculations.

When using the diagnostic structure, be sure to include severity of illness. In the procedure-driven indemnity system, providers have tended to overstate the condition in order to avoid being limited in length of stay or coverage. In our diagnostic example of the sprain, the severity came in three degrees: mild, moderate, and severe. Your severity index must be logical, standard, and consistently applied.

Even though there will always be some subjectivity in assigning severity, consistency in selection of severity criteria will eliminate much statistical bias. Using our example of back pain from Chapter 3, I have created the following diagnostically structured statement, which will systematize data entry:

> The patient is suffering from a *trauma*-induced left-lateral L5/S1 *disk prolapse* with attendant frequent moderate grade 3 [meaning to the level of the foot] left-sided *sciatic* radiation, constant moderate *back pain*, grade 3 *muscle spasm*, and occasional *urinary incontinence*, which is further complicated by *obesity*.

The key elements of the diagnosis are:

1. Dynamic of injury: trauma (accident).
2. Tissue of causation: disk prolapse.
3. Attendant factors: grade 3 sciatica; grade 3 muscle spasm; occasional urinary incontinence.
4. Complicating factors: obesity.

The key socioeconomic factors (SEFs) taken from the patient's chart would be age, sex, race, and education. (Income has also been identified as a key socioeconomic factor, but it is questionable whether you can collect it with ease or accuracy. The reason income is an SEF is that people with higher incomes do not want to take the time required to wait for a doctor. In economic terms, the opportunity cost for them is too high. They prefer to be elsewhere making money; thus, they tend to use less care.)

So as a result of your file reviews, you have collected the following information on each of your several hundred patients:

Dynamic of injury.
Tissue of causation.
Attendant factors.
Complicating factors.

Socioeconomic factors: age, sex, race, education, income. ICD and/or DRG code.

This data becomes the basis for an actuarial study. To this you must now add financial data, namely, costs of procedures and length of stay. You could add procedures such as MRIs, CTs, bone scans, laboratory tests, NCVs, EMGs, or anything that can influence treatment and cost pathways; this would also begin the data collection needed for outcome and clinical variation studies. You can now filter the data to determine if relationships between them exist and how CSCs and SEFs affect treatment and cost pathways.

What type of software is necessary to manipulate the data? Of course, there are complex programs that will do great and wonderful things with the data collected. They are also expensive and difficult to run for the most part. Some over-the-counter software exists that will also do an excellent job. They include Microsoft Access, dBase, Panorama, and Paradox. However, once you collect the information, you will need to analyze it for statistical significance. This means data must be transferred to a statistical program such as InStat for calculation. Several programs exist that could do both database functions and statistical calculations, such as SPSS, an old mainframe program. SPSS is powerful, but it proves difficult for many, including myself, to use.

For most uses, Excel, a common spreadsheet program, is my choice. Although spreadsheet programs are more along the line of list managers than true databases, for our purposes Excel's database functions will do nicely for quite a while. Two texts to use in understanding Excel's database functions are *Excel for Dummies* and *Running Microsoft Excel 5.*[5]

The point of the database is to establish whether or not relationships exist between the different data fields. For example, the existence of a suspected relationship between severity of illness and costs could be determined. Costs associated with a particular doctor could be tracked. Given a population's demographics, comparisons concerning the costs of specific protocols for a similar population under your care, for a particular diagnosis, and for a particular doctor could be made.

As your expertise with the database increases, your prediction accuracy will increase. You can also generate outcome and clinical variation studies to improve prediction accuracy, which is extremely helpful in negotiating a managed care contract. The end result of the data analyses described in this chapter would be a list detailing all the factors involved in a diagnosis and treatment. The complete list for our example would look something like this:

Dynamic of injury.

Tissue of causation.

Attendant factors.

Complicating factors.

Socioeconomic factors: age, sex, race, education, income.

Procedures rendered (list in separate fields): MRI, CT, bone scans, laboratory tests, NCV, EMG.

Total cost.

Outcome rating.

Doctor's name.

ICD and/or DRG code

REFERENCES

1. L. Iezzoni, M. Schwartz, A. Ash, Y. Mackiernan, and E. Hotchkin, "Risk Adjustment Methods Can Affect Perceptions of Outcome," *American Journal of Medical Quality* 9, no. 2 (Summer 1994), pp. 43–48.

2. Francine Gaillour, "Leading Physicians to the Head of the Class in Managed Care," *MGMA Journal* 42, no. 2, pp. 15–20.

3. H. Sutton and A. Sorbo, *Actuarial Issues in the Fee-For-Service/ Prepaid Medical Group* (Englewood, CO: Center for Research in Ambulatory Health Care Administration, 1993).

4. Lawrence Benson, *Managing Capitation and Risk* (Nashville, TN: Business Network, 1994).

5. G. Harvey, *Excel 5 for Dummies* (Foster City, CA: IDG Books Worldwide, 1994) the Cobb Group, *Running Microsoft Excel 5* (Redmond, WA: Microsoft Press, 1994).

8
C H A P T E R

Activity-Based Costing

The purpose of this book is to provide a method of collecting accurate data for statistical prediction in capitated and managed care environments. Accuracy in large part depends on the provider's accounting methods. Utilization predictions of the frequency and length of stay of services must reflect the true cost of providing treatment. To arrive at a frequency of treatment and length of stay for a particular diagnosis properly adjusted for complicating factors, severity of illness, and co-morbidities (CSCs) and socioeconomic factors (SEFs) without accurately determining costs would be like returning a kickoff in football 99 yards in the last minute of the game only to fumble and lose the ball at the goal line.

Unfortunately, the traditional accounting methods used by the majority of offices do not ensure accurate cost predictions. Historically, providers have used accounting principles more suited to a manufacturing environment. These principles do not translate well to the business of medicine. Further, most physicians magnify the problems resulting from this ill fit by viewing managerial accounting in an overly simplistic fashion. First, they tend to see themselves collecting higher fee payments than is realistic or factual; second, they tend to see all expenses as static and fixed. This simplistic view is based on the following equations:

$$\text{Number of patient visits} \times \text{Charges per visit} = \text{Total charges}$$
$$\text{Total charges} - \text{Expenses} = \text{Gross profit}$$

THE BUSINESS OF MEDICINE

Most physicians lack business training. As a result, they have been labeled as poor businesspeople. As a group, this is true. I was attending a board meeting of a group of 14 physicians. The topic of accounts receivable and collection rates came up. I asked the group what their collection rate was. Without hesitation, one physician said the group's rate was about 96 percent. When I asked why the collection rate was so high, the physician replied, "After we write off all the adjustments and bad debts, that is about what it is." The unfortunate part of this encounter was that no one else on the board saw the problem with the answer I was given.

The highly competitive nature of the current managed care marketplace is forcing greater numbers of physicians to learn the business of medicine, or hire someone else to do it for them.

Credit-Based Structure

The easiest way to understand the business of medicine is to realize that medicine is a credit-granting institution. Services are provided today and collected at some future point. This credit process is based on the patients' potential insurance benefits. The different credit types make up what is known as a payer mix.

The current payer mix for most offices consists of cash, major medical, worker's compensation, Medicare, Medicaid, and third-party payers (e.g., for auto accidents or falls). Major medical is currently being subdivided into managed care plans, and capitated plans, further complicating the credit-based accounting procedures in offices. Figure 8–1 presents the credit issues involved with various payer types.

Worker's compensation (WC) is a typical payer type. It is a federal program that is administered on a state level. Each state

FIGURE 8–1

Payer Mix

Payer Type	Credit Issues
Worker's Compensation	Paperwork, authorization, fixed fees, treatment length restrictions, complex administrative procedures, opportunity cost of money.
Major medical	Paperwork, usual and customary fees, treatment length restrictions, copayments, deductibles, cost of time.
Medicare and Medicaid	Paperwork, fixed fees, treatment length restrictions, complex administrative procedures, opportunity cost of money, copayments, deductibles, and penalties.
Third-party liability	Reimbursement depends on issues of recoverability from another. Issues are liability, damages, "deep pockets," and opportunity cost of money.
Cash	Collectability affected by amount of charges and wealth of customer.
Managed care	Paperwork, authorization, fixed fees, treatment length restrictions, complex administrative procedures, copayments, deductibles, and opportunity cost of money.

has interpreted and implements the federal law differently. Thus, coverage and benefits under WC vary from state to state. In California, worker's compensation covers qualified workers who have suffered injuries "arising out of or caused by his employment" (AOE/COE). Worker's compensation coverage provides for reasonable and medically necessary treatment to return the worker to his or her pre-injury status.

Treatment generally falls into one of two major classifications: disputed or nondisputed. Nondisputed usually means that the provider will be paid at some point down the line if he or she has followed all of the other rules and procedures. The primary rule to follow is obtaining authorization and, thus, medical control. Care of a nondisputed injured worker may be authorized or nonauthorized.

Authorized care means the patient has been given permission to begin treatment at the facility having medical control. (In reality, physicians who receive carrier-authorized referrals abdicate some degree of medical control, usually as it relates to frequency or length of stay, back to the carrier in an attempt to ensure a continuing supply of authorized patients. The carrier uses this mechanism to control costs.)

Nonauthorized care may be compensated, but it usually involves legal proceedings to force payment. Credit in these cases is extended on a lien basis. This liening process can be risky, especially if the office is unfamiliar with the entire worker's compensation process. Many times I have seen entire medical bills amounting to thousands of dollars be tossed out by the judge or an attorney in worker's compensation court because of minor problems in the medical office's paperwork.

Disputed claims arise with questions concerning the qualifications of the worker, the AOE/COE status of the injury, the necessity of medical care, the medical control, the notification and reporting process, the authorization process, or a myriad of other issues. The physician can continue treatment in such cases on a lien basis.

Thus, the physician's office and staff, through the worker's compensation system, have become part of a government-run insurance system. The provider must meet responsibilities within that system if he or she expects to receive payment. Any faulty paperwork or procedure jeopardizes the collectability of an account.

FIGURE 8-2

Complex Dynamic of Payer Mix

Number of patient visits	×	Charges per visit	=	Total charges
Payer Types		Fee Issues		
Worker's compensation		Fixed fees		As adjusted by credit issues
Major medical		Usual and customary fees + copayments + deductibles		
Medicare and Medicaid		Fixed fees + Copayments + deductibles		
Third-party liability		Usual fees		
Cash		What the market will bear		
Managed care		Fixed fees + copayments + deductibles		

As worker's compensation has become a complex system of granting credit to patients based upon several subclassifications, so has major medical become complex, fragmenting into a variety of managed care plans, each with its own special paperwork and procedural requirements. The requirement of a physician's staff to fill out paperwork and follow set procedures in order to collect fees is a major reason for rising medical costs.

Figure 8–2 expands the first equation presented earlier to reflect a more complex dynamic. Because of a lack of business training, physicians have tended to view expenses and cash flows simplisticly. As the payer mix (credit basis of patients) becomes more complex and profit margins shrink, often the result of discounted or fixed-fee schedules of some form of managed care, providers' accounting systems must more accurately address variations in fee collection and rates.

COST ACCOUNTING AND BUDGET PREDICTIONS

Costing is an important part of overhead control. Accurate costing is even more important in managed care, where profit margins are smaller. As mentioned in the previous chapter, traditional accounting is the basis for fee-for-service actuarial determination and activity-based costing is the basis for the budgetary or cost method.

To understand costing and pricing concepts, let's explore a hypothetical situation of my running a small practice with two hourly employees and one doctor. The practice provides only two procedures, X and Y. Each employee works 160 hours per month at $20 per hour and time and a half for overtime. Each employee can produce 160 units of X procedure and 640 units of Y procedure per month. Fixed overhead, including lease payments and administration costs, is $8,000 per month. The patient charge for procedure X is $72; Y is $27. The collection rate is 72 percent. My employees are currently working to capacity, with no overtime allowed. Variable cost for materials is $10 per unit for procedure X and $3 per unit for Y. The employees do all components of the procedure, including setup. The doctor performs the postprocedure follow-up.

As shown in Figure 8–3, the practice's total production capacity is $28,800. At 72 percent, collections are $20,736. The total

FIGURE 8–3

Income and Expenses for Hypothetical Office

Income per Month		
Procedure X		
160 units × $72 = $11,520.00		
Procedure Y		
640 units × $27 = 17,280.00		
Total charges	$28,800.00	
Collection rate	72%	
Net income	$20,736.00	
Expenses per Month		
Fixed costs		$ 8,000.00
Variable costs		
Two employees × $20/hr. × 40hrs/wk. =		6,400.00
Y costs = $3/unit × 640	=	1,920.00
X costs = $10/unit × 160	=	1,600.00
Total expenses		$17,920.00
Profit		$ 2,816.00

costs (fixed costs + variable costs) are $17,920. Profit is calculated to be $2,816 per month.

White Knight Managed Care then enters the market and contracts with several large employers in the area. White Knight has promised to cut insurance rates to these employers by its cost-saving methods. This will affect 25 percent of my current patients. I'll now be payed for services rendered to them through this managed care arrangement. White Knight contracts directly with select physicians, including me, guaranteeing to pay for services at 100 percent of it's usual reasonable and customary fee schedule. White Knight's fee for procedure X is 75 percent of my usual fee and 65 percent for procedure Y. There is no copayment requirement.

Figure 8–4 shows how this managed care arrangement affects my business. I now bring in $15,552 per month through my original pay arrangements and $4,468 through managed care, totaling $20,520 per month. Thus, my monthly profit drops by about 8 per-

FIGURE 8–4

Income per Month after Managed Care Arrangement

Office Billing	
Procedure X	
120 units × $72	= $ 8,640.00
Procedure Y	
480 units × $27	= 12,960.00
Total charges	$ 21,600.00
Collection rate	72%
Income from office billing	$ 15,552.00
White Knight Managed Care Payments	
Procedure X	
40 units × $54.00	= $ 2,160.00
Procedure Y	
160 units × $17.55	= 2,808.00
Total managed care payments	$ 4,968.00
Net income	$ 20,520.00
Total expenses (see Figure 8–3)	17,920.00
Profit	$ 2,600.00

cent, to $2,600. At this point, I must either accept the loss or try to raise regular fees to make up for the loss.

To stay competitive, I lease a new piece of diagnostic equipment at a price of $600 per month. At the same time, I receive notice of a cost-of-living rent increase of $250 per month. Also, I give my employees a cost-of-living increase, raising their hourly rate to $22.00 per hour each. Figure 8–5 shows the new projected monthly budget. Profit is now 43 percent of what it was under managed care with only an 8 percent increase in overhead.

But besides White Knight's managed care contract and the expense increases, other events affect my business. One competitor has decided to retire; another, after taking Spanish lessons, is moving to Mexico to start a cash practice. I anticipate my patient flow will increase about 30 percent. The payer mix will be the same percentage as my current one. Of course, I will need to hire more staff and expand my office to accommodate the new patient flow. This increases my rent by another $1,000, raising my total fixed costs to $9,850.

What's more, my administrator informed me that due to the increased paperwork required by managed care we had to hire another fixed-salary staff member. The cost is about $1,500 per month. The good news is the new staffer in collections has increased my collection rate on my indemnity practice to 83 percent. The question is, How many people should I hire to handle the increase in the patient flow?

FIGURE 8–5

Projected Monthly Expenses with Cost-of-Living Increases

Fixed costs		$ 8,000.00
+ Rent increase		250.00
+ New equipment		600.00
Variable costs		
Two employees × $22/hr. × 40 hr./wk. × 4 wks.	=	$ 7,040.00
Y costs $3/unit × 640	=	1,920.00
X costs $10/unit × 160	=	1,600.00
Total expenses		$ 19,410.00
Net income		$ 20,520.00
Profit		$ 1,110.00

Since two employees can produce 160 units of procedure X and 640 units of Y, one employee can produce 80 units of X and 320 units of Y. My 30 percent increase in business suggests that procedure X will be increased by 48 units and Y by 192 units. I could hire a part-time employee, but the one I want will take only full-time at $24.00 per hour. This position is hard to fill, and if I pass on this employee I might regret it. As a result, I hire this person and have to give my staff raises to the same level to keep them happy. My recalculated budget now looks better, as shown in Figure 8–6.

I hire a consultant who tells me that I have underutilized em-

FIGURE 8–6

Revised Budget Resulting from Increased Patient Flow

Income per Month		
Office billing		
Procedure X		
156 units × $72	=	$ 11,232.00
Procedure Y		
624 units × $27	=	16,848.00
Total charges		$ 28,080.00
Collection rate		83%
Income from office billing		$ 23,306.40
Managed Care		
Procedure X		
52 units × $54	=	$ 2,808.00
Procedure Y		
208 units × $17.55	=	3,650.40
Total managed care payments		$ 6,458.40
Net income		$ 29,764.80
Expenses per Month		
Fixed costs		$ 9,850.00
Variable costs		
Three employees × $24/hr. × 40 hr./wk. × 4 wks.	=	$ 11,520.00
Y costs $3/unit × 832	=	2,496.00
X costs $10/unit × 208	=	2,080.00
Total expenses		$ 25,946.00
Profit		$ 3,818.80

ployees; as such, I have what is known as excess capacity. She recommends that I start providing procedure Z, which will remove excess capacity and provide extra income. We determine that my new employee can perform the new procedure, including setup. White Knight Manage Care will reimburse the procedure at 74 percent of my usual fee of $46. Material cost for procedure Z is $15 per unit. I'm now once again functioning at full capacity. My budget looks great, as shown in Figure 8–7.

My budget model has shown me that to achieve maximum profit, I must minimize excess capacity. Expanding services and acquiring competitors are good ways to do this. Using the model prepared, I can now project costs if another insurance company should enter the market. It is essential to remember that increased competition leads to smaller margins. Survival in a market of shrinking margins means you must grow to capitalize on the concept of large numbers. This concept is followed by insurance companies since they lose money on people who use their policies. To offset this loss, insurance companies insure large numbers of people. Those people who don't use their insurance coverage pay for those who do. Thus, insurance companies can use the principle of large numbers to their advantage.

I can extend that principle to my office. To survive in a market where margins are getting smaller, a business must often grow bigger.

Let's now look at the budgets again. White Knight Managed Care has introduced a new product, an at-risk plan. White Knight has inquired if I will provide X, Y, and Z services for its at-risk plan. The company serves a population of 18,000 people, who according to their actuarial studies will need 52 units of procedure X, 208 units of Y, and 32 units of Z. White Knight will be eliminating its discounted fee-for-service plan completely.

What per patient per month (PPPM) figure can my office take and remain profitable? The obvious way is to use the value of $7,518.24 (from Figure 8–7) and divide it by the population of 18,000 to arrive at a cap rate of 42 cents per patient per month. It is a very rough method of determining PPPM. But essentially, this is the fee-for-service method. There are variations to this method. For example, I can convert our X, Y, and Z procedures into a numeric value by looking at the relative value unit associated with it and dividing it into the total amount of money we need to receive. But

FIGURE 8–7

Revised Budget with Additional Procedure

Income per Month		
Office billing		
Procedure X		
156 units × $72	=	$ 11,232.00
Procedure Y		
624 units × $27	=	16,848.00
Procedure Z		
105 units × $46	=	4,830.00
Total charges		$ 32,910.00
Collection rate		83%
Income from office billing		$ 27,315.30
Managed Care		
Procedure X		
52 units × $54	=	$ 2,808.00
Procedure Y		
208 units × $17.55	=	3,650.40
Procedure Z		
32 units × $33.12	=	1,059.84
Total managed care payments		$ 7,518.24
Net income		$ 34,833.54
Expenses per Month		
Fixed costs		$ 9,850.00
Variable costs		
Three employees × $24/hr. × 40 hr./wk. × 4 wks.	=	$ 11,520.00
Y costs $3/unit × 832 units	=	2,496.00
X costs $10/unit × 208 units	=	2,080.00
Z costs $15/unit × 137 units	=	2,055.00
Total expenses		$ 28,001.00
Profit		$ 6,832.54

the effect is the same: capitation fees are based upon frequency of services and fee-for-service equivalent charges.

In the introductory discussion of the structure of our hypothetical office and standard costs of services, I noted that my employees performed procedural setup and the doctor performed the postprocedure follow-up. What would happen if less expensive personnel were used to do setup or postprocedures? Experience dictates that the use of physician assistants would produce a cost savings.

The incorporation of an assistant to do setup procedures and free a more trained and expensive employee to do a greater number of procedures would be desirable so long as it did not produce excess capacity or lower-quality service. If a less expensive employee is used in setup procedures, I could have maintained my $22 per hour labor rate and saved the difference. For example, a lesser experienced or specialized employee might be paid $15 per hour compared to the $22 presently being paid. This $7 differential would account for a savings of $2,080 (see Figure 8–8).

The actual savings would be greater because of other factors such as training costs, employer matching taxes, and employee replacement costs; but the point is, substitution of lesser paid employees leads to great savings.

Extending the cost of the employees over the number of units produced is another way of examining production costing. Let's say that the relative value units (RVUs) for the three procedures, X, Y, and Z, are .6, .4, and 1.2 units, respectively. The total relative value units produced by the office would be 622:

$$208 \text{ X units} \times .6 = 124.8$$
$$832 \text{ Y units} \times .4 = 332.80$$
$$137 \text{ Z units} \times 1.2 = \underline{164.40}$$
$$622.00 \text{ RVUs}$$

FIGURE 8–8

Sample Budgetary Costing Method

Fixed costs		$ 9,850.00
Variable costs		
Two employees × $22/hr. × 40 hr./wk. × 4 wks.	=	$ 7,040.00
One employee × $15/hr. × 40 hr./wk. × 4 wks.	=	2,400.00
Y costs $3/unit × 832	=	2,496.00
X costs $10/unit × 208	=	2,080.00
Z costs $15/unit × 137	=	2,055.00
Total expenses		$ 25,921.00
Expenses from Figure 8–7		$ 28,001.00
Savings		$ 2,080.00

The costs for producing our service with three of the higher-cost employees would be the total employee costs divided by the total number of RVUs, or $18.52 per RVU. This compares unfavorably to the $15.18 per RVU achieved with a less expensive employee. This is close to a 20 percent savings.

This allocation of costs over the number of full-time equivalent employees (FTEs) needed to produce services is the basis of the budgetary or cost method. The conversion of services into RVUs is a way of estimating production cost equivalents for services.

For example, Double Dare Insurance Co. wishes to contract for fully capitated services. It will pay my office $13.13 PPPM for a population of 8,000. This will be in addition to my current patient base. Should I accept the contract?

Additional income is easy to calculate. It is simply PPPM rate times the number of patients. In this case the additional income is $105,040. The total income is now $139,873.54 (see Figure 8–9).

The utilization rates for a covered population of 1,000 is projected to use 620 units of procedure X, 257 units of Y, and 210 units of Z. On the basis of the RVU values previously given, my office would need to produce 726.80 RVUs per 1,000 patients, or 5,814.4 RVUs to cover the total 8,000 population.

$$620 \text{ units of } X \times .6 = 372.00$$
$$257 \text{ units of } Y \times .4 = 102.80$$
$$210 \text{ units of } Z \times 1.2 = \underline{252.00}$$
$$726.80 \text{ RVUs per 1,000 patients}$$

Given the current employee efficiency as calculated with three employees is 207.33 RVUs per employee (622 RVUs/3 employees), it will take 28.04 FTEs to meet the demands of the contract (5,814.4 RVUs/207.33 RVUs per employee). There are two hiring options. The first is to hire 29 highly trained employees at an average rate of $24 per hour. The second is to hire a combination of employees who can produce the number of units needed. For example, 10 can be the $15 per hour type and 19 the $24 per hour type. Since only 28.04 employees are needed, both hiring options result in excess capacity. Cost comparisons appear in Figure 8–10. The combined method of hiring produces a monthly savings of $14,400.

Because of the increased patient and administrative load resulting from the Double Dare contract, I needed to hire additional

FIGURE 8–9

Income per Month Including Capitated Care
Payments

Office Billing		
Procedure X		
156 units × $72	= $	11,232.00
Procedure Y		
624 units × $27	=	16,848.00
Procedure Z		
105 units × $46	=	4,830.00
Total charges		$ 32,910.00
Collection rate		83%
Income from office billing		$ 27,315.30
Managed Care (White Knight)		
Procedure X		
52 units × $54	= $	2,808.00
Procedure Y		
208 units × $17.55	=	3,650.40
Procedure Z		
32 units × $33.12	=	1,059.84
Total managed care payments		$ 7,518.24
Capitate Care (Double Dare)		
$13.13 PPPM × 8,000	=	$ 105,040.00
Net income from all sources		$ 139,873.54

administrative staff members and purchase additional equipment. The new projected expenses appear in Figure 8–11.

The projected profit with the inclusion of the at-risk, fully capitated contract are illustrated in Figure 8–12. The increased profit is $209, hardly worth the headaches involved in providing the services.

Other problems exist with this contract. The basis of the actuarial study need to be considered. Remember, Double Dare offers proof of utilization that is unadjusted for complications, severity, and co-morbidities. Comparison of my experiential data to Double Dare's actuarial data might, and probably will, show differences. I

F I G U R E 8–10

Cost Comparison of Hiring Options

29 employees × $24/hr. × 40 hr./wk. × 4 wks. =	$ 111,360.00
versus	
10 employees × $15/hr. × 40 hr./wk. × 4 wks. =	24,000.00
19 employees × $24/hr. × 40 hr./wk. × 4 wks. =	72,960.00
	$ 96,960.00
Savings of $14,400.00	

must take Double Dare's numbers with a grain of salt. If I'm in doubt, I should be conservative and either not take the contract or insist on an escape clause in the contract.

On the positive side, I may be able to maximize profit by several strategies. First, I may be able to practice preventive medicine and lower total utilization. Second, with the greater volume of supplies needed I may be able to purchase materials at a lower cost. Third, clinical variation and outcome studies may make me more efficient and consistent in resource utilization. Additionally, eliminating excess capacity and maximizing collection (credit) policies may provide greater profit. One final consideration is that

F I G U R E 8–11

Projected Monthly Expenses for Managed and Capitated Care Contracts

Fixed costs	$12,000	
+ Cost of living + new equipment	2,000	$ 14,000.00
Variable costs		
22 employees × $24/hr. × 40 hr./wk. × 4 wks. =		84,480.00
11 employees × $10/hr. × 40 hr./wk. × 4 wks. =		17,600.00
Y costs $3/unit × 1,089	=	3,267.00
X costs $10/unit × 828	=	8,280.00
Z costs $15/unit × 347	=	5,205.00
Total expenses per month		$ 132,832.00

FIGURE 8–12

Comparison of Projected Profits

Before at-Risk Contract		After at-Risk Contract	
Income		Income	
Indemnity	$ 27,315.30	Indemnity	$ 27,315.30
White Knight	34,833.54	White Knight	34,833.54
	$ 34,833.54	Double Dare	105,040.00
			$139,873.54
Expenses		Expenses	
Fixed	$ 9,850.00	Fixed	$ 14,000.00
Variable	18,151.00	Variable	118,832.00
	$ 28,001.00		$132,832.00
Profit	$ 6,832.54		$ 7,041.54

a larger provider may attract more business and contracts and may be an acquisition target.

As I stated in the opening, the purpose of this chapter is to introduce ways of costing services accurately and combining that information with CSC- and SEF-adjusted data in the in-office database. The information derived from a file review can be entered along with the cost of patient treatment into the database. This data will allow a variety of estimates to be performed.

Data collected in this manner have two main advantages: first, the data are adjusted for CSC factors, which can help the provider identify outliers earlier and thus prevent large aggregate losses. Second, the data are adjusted for socioeconomic factors, which adds tremendous accuracy power to utilization prediction.

These factors combined with activity-based budgeting will allow a provider to make accurate production predictions. It must be borne in mind, however, that actual production costs can, and probably will, vary from projected costs, favorably or unfavorably. All data are subject to error. It is best to be conservative until confidence and experience are gained, but the process of adjusting for CSC and socioeconomic factors together with activity-based costing will provide the physician with the most accurate reflection of his in-office experience.

9
CHAPTER

Managed Care
Contracting Considerations

In the past, a physician could decide whom he or she would accept as patients and under what conditions of potential insurance benefits he or she would grant credit. In managed care contracting, the patient pool is preselected. The physician's ability to eliminate patients from the pool is very limited. In exchange for participation in the managed care system, the physician gives up certain rights to the carrier. In this system, the carrier retains risk and, as such, is interested in controlling utilization.

In fully capitated care, the burden of loss and risk is more on the physician than the carrier, hence the physician must be able to control patient selection and utilization. Outliers in the patient pool, those who utilize a disproportionate amount of resources, must be identified early to minimize loss. The provider can then issue stop-loss claims on outliers, which limit and shift loss back to the carrier. The key to outlier identification, thus a main line of defense against loss, is in-office data adjusted for complicating factors, severity of illness, and co-morbidities.

Managed care and capitated care contracting offer potential for profit. However, most forms of managed care can offer less risk, both legally and financially, for the physician than full capitation. Yet following the financial principles of investment, capitated care should offer a potential for greater profit since risk is higher. But does it? Let's explore the risks involved.

PROBLEMS IN CONTRACTING

Contracts have several traditional components: an obligation portion, a benefits portion, and a portion detailing a solution should something go wrong with the contract. Although not expressed here in typical legal terminology, these components should be present in every contract a physician agrees to. These components cut both ways, imposing requirements on the provider and the carrier. Often, contracts offered by a party lack one or more of these components in an attempt to gain advantage over the other party. However, to help ensure success of an undertaking, a contract should provide structure and rules to work by to achieve a common goal; anything short of this should give one pause to consider the motivations of the other contracting party, and it almost always leads to future problems.

The motivation of both the provider and the carrier should be to provide the insured population with the best care at the cheapest price while earning maximum profit with the least administrative and legal problems possible. Since profit is the prime motivation of both, it makes them competitors.

Another problem in managed care and capitated care contracting is that the playing field is not level. The carrier has a major bargaining advantage, that is, control of the patient pool. The provider has several other disadvantages. For one, other competitors are likely to want the contract. Many providers have little, if any, experience in the business of insurance. Also, the provider has no control over the contract between the carrier and the patient pool, which contains several unknown characteristics.

It is important to define an insured, or covered, population by socioeconomic factors as most groups have a recognized utilization pattern. An insurance carrier offers a specific product, a policy, to a targeted group. The provider must compare the carrier's utilization data for that targeted group to the in-office data collected. Any significant variance between the data that suggests underestimation on the part of the carrier is reason for concern. Stop-loss or other escape clauses can protect the provider should the in-office figures turn out to be correct.

Additionally, the insurance carrier must be prevented from expanding the target market to include other population groups with different socioeconomic factors. Some carriers have sold policies created for one market to other markets in an attempt to turn a losing product into a profitable one. For example, imagine what would happen if a policy targeted to a relatively healthy group would be offered to an older group. Although the carrier could conceivably collect more, the physician may be stuck providing for the older group with a higher utilization at a lower contracted fee.

Certain carriers have used another form of substitution, known as ghosting. In a ghosting situation, a physician treating a population of patients for carrier A may find that he or she has been given some patients from carrier B under an agreement between the two carriers. There is no guarantee that the B population has the same socioeconomic factors as the A population.

After taking measures to define the socioeconomic factors of a target population, the provider must address the problem of complicating factors, severity of illness, and co-morbidities (CSCs). The actuarial studies offered by the carrier will specify the incidence rate expected for the defined group as determined by ICD codes collected from HCFA 1500 claim forms. But these studies are not adjusted for CSC factors. Again, the only protection against risk for a provider is to have adequate stop-loss mechanisms in place.

THE POLICY AND UTILIZATION

Most contracting physicians have failed to thoroughly explore policies as a source of problems. A policy can hide many elements that will affect utilization. A prime problem concerns the specification of the covered population. Most healthcare policies are offered through employers. The people in this group are, for the most part, healthy. Their families, however, present unknowns. Every assumed healthy covered worker has one to three unknowns attached to him or her. This multiplies the risk of contracting enormously. If a policy is written to cover family and dependents, how is *dependent* defined? Is an elderly parent living with the family a dependent?

This issue involves what is known as the agency problem. The agency problem is a concept from finance to indicate the conflict of interest that arises when a manager of a stock has to make a choice between the interest of the issuing agency and the interest of the investor. In my opinion, the physician is investing (in the form of contracted labor for a fixed price) in the insurance carrier. Financial contracts limit agency problems by the inclusion of restrictive covenants and the designation of trustees to ensure compliance. In healthcare contracting no such trustees exist. The provider must take measures to ensure that the carrier does not substitute patients or change the market for which it is contracting.

What is not covered under a policy is as important as covered items. Certain illnesses or pre-existing conditions might not be covered; specific services or treatments might be excluded. The provider must carefully examine the policy to determine if the carrier has liberally written it for easy sale to the public. For example, if the policy states that routine services are covered at no cost to the patient, the provider will face the risk of bearing that cost, which could be substantial. Or say a policy carries low deductibles and copayments; these features help sell the policy, but they lead to greater utilization.

It should be obvious that the more generous the policy, the greater the risk for the provider. However, liability issues present the potential for an even greater financial downside.

PHYSICIAN LIABILITY IN MANAGED CARE

Physicians hesitate to enter contracts for several reasons. Financial risks are chief among the concerns, but recent lawsuits over coverage that guarantees access to technology, treatment, and referral have raised new questions about managed care contracting. Although many of the liability issues in managed care exist only theoretically, and have not resulted in actual lawsuits, they have affected physician behavior in contracting.

Whether real or not, the potential for lawsuits has already shaken the managed care environment. A Murietta, California, woman who had requested a controversial bone marrow transplant for her metastatic breast cancer died without receiving the therapy. Her insurance company, Health Net of Woodland Hills, California, refused the request, calling the treatment experimental. The family members filed suit, claiming that the physician had raised their expectations by suggesting the radical treatment (*de-Meurers* v. *Health Net*). They felt they were entitled to whatever treatment they desired. An arbitration board found that Health Net should have paid for the therapy and awarded the family 89 million dollars.[1]

In a similar case, a federal appeals court in Richmond, Virginia, found that facilities and physicians must treat a patient, and insurance carriers must pay for the treatment, if the family members insist, even in hopeless cases.[2]

In a now-famous case filed against the State of California (*Wicklines* v. *California*), a Medi-Cal patient suffering from a postoperative complication was denied an eight-day extension of length of stay in opposition to the surgeon's advise. Given a four-day extension instead and released, she subsequently developed gangrene and lost her leg. She brought suit against Medi-Cal and won. What is important about this case is that the physician had not formally objected to Medi-Cal's LOS determination. The appellate court judge pointed out that had the patient also brought suit against the physician, he would have been found negligent.[3]

As a result of *Wicklines* v. *California,* some managed care plans have dropped California physicians who follow this judge's opinion from their list of providers. Another result of the case is that physicians cannot avoid responsibility to the patient should the insurance company deny services. Thus, physicians face both financial and liability risk.

Gatekeeper liability is a new type that has arisen with managed care. Gatekeeper liability is founded on the concept that a physician under pressure to limit referrals may try to treat a condition beyond his or her competence.[4] Physician behaviors that might provide a basis for such lawsuits are failure to diagnose and failure to refer. Although still largely theoretical, several gatekeeper liability suits have been filed.

Hold-harmless clauses are probably the most common source of liability. These clauses transfer liability to the physician. Some hold-harmless clauses are so broad that physicians could be held liable for denial of benefits dictated by a managed care plan,[5] as in *deMeurers* v. *Health Net* and *Wicklines* v. *California.* These clauses also provide that the physician would have to pay the carrier's legal fees. In a final insult, hold-harmless clauses often invalidate the physician's malpractice insurance.[6]

In the course of doing business with a managed care company, physicians are often required to serve on credentialing, utilization, or peer review committees. These committees present a variety of potential liabilities. Credentialing exposes a physician to liability for the actions of others. For example, say the negligence of an incompetent person precipitates a lawsuit; the physicians on the committee that credentialed the person are potentially liable.

Physicians on utilization and peer review committees are also susceptible to liability suits. Their actions may be responsible for the denial of care to an individual. Unfortunately, committee work is another area to which malpractice insurance does not extend. Additional coverage for "errors and omission" and utilization review (UR) liability is needed.[7]

Another area in which physicians are left holding the bag is in joint and several liability. In many states, a physician may be jointly and severally responsible for the debts of another. For example, if an uninsured physician in a group practice loses a malpractice suit, his or her colleagues could end up paying for the loss. It is essential that physicians carry sufficient malpractice or liability coverage.[8]

Managed care contracts may sometimes contain a fee agreement known as a most-favored-nation clause, in which preferential rates are offered by a provider. However, a most-favored-nation clause may violate Medicare law, which entitles patients to a provider's lowest rate. Federal and state governments will often set minimum managed care fees for doctors through Medicare's worker's compensation provision.

A contract can have many hidden liabilities. These are often found in sections addressing operating procedures or practice guidelines. A physician is obligated to follow the standards outlined in any contract he or she accepts. The problem is that standards and procedures frequently change, hence contracts don't typically detail specific protocols; instead, they present general guidelines. Very often the physician does not know what the standards and procedures are. This can result in what is known as incorporation by reference liability.[9]

Other hidden liabilities for physicians can result from actions of the carrier to the public, such as advertising claims of extraordinary care or service. A patient might perceive a failure of the physician to deliver upon a promise of the carrier.

Failure of a carrier to be patient-friendly may harm the physician's credibility and trust. Establishing a strong patient–doctor relationship is a prime factor in reducing malpractice claims. Recently, Kaiser Permanente attempted to counter what it perceived as an increasingly hostile media attitude toward managed care. An advertisement by Kaiser boasted, "We're not like other HMOs." In a related action, 56 physicians called for the recall of Kaiser Permanente's regional executive director, charging that he has made "drastic cuts" that harm "the caregiver–patient relationship."[10]

Finally, in the past a physician could dismiss what he or she perceived as a problem patient with adequate notice; not so with managed care, which has its own bureaucratic "due process." This due process can become quite elaborate, with subclassifications distinguishing between abusive, disruptive, noncompliant, and the nonpaying patients. Multiple notifications and phone calls are made by the carrier, often worsening a situation. Bear in mind that angry patients are the ones who bring suit.[11]

Changes in the Legal Environment

As managed care has established a 34 percent market penetration in California, making interaction with such firms an eventuality, several consumer and provider protection bills have been signed into law. HMOs argue that these laws increase costs. The new laws mandate that medically trained personnel review physician's treatment decisions, that increased requirements be met prior to releasing a doctor from an HMO panel, and that HMOs disclose distribution of premium dollars.[12]

Not to be left out, the American Medical Association (AMA) has drafted and proposed a Patient Protection Act. The prime proposals of this act follow:

1. Carriers must pay for out-of-network expenses incurred by patients.
2. A special committee must be established to participate in the structuring and running of the care plan.
3. Carriers must provide detailed denial information to physicians.
4. Carriers must provide due process information to physicians on application and release procedures.
5. Employers must offer HMO, PPO, indemnity insurance, or a medical savings account.[13]

At first glance, the AMA's proposals seem to call for more physician control of insurance plans while offering little protection to consumers. In addition, if implemented the proposals would likely eliminate some liability for physicians.

In summary, physicians are at a distinct disadvantage in dealing with managed care carriers. Managed care contracting increases physician liability. Solutions are few, with some predicated on the physician's ability to insist upon review and disclosure of operations' procedures and policies. To lessen liability, elements of the system that are not within control of the physician—such as the process involved in denial, dismissal, and contractual disputes—must be changed. Although some new laws may begin to curb liability and, at the same time, protect consumers, little if any real liability protection is seen in the near future. Worse yet is that physicians have little or no market share, thus they have no power to force real change in managed care contracts.

REFERENCES

1. E. Larson, "The Soul of an HMO," *Time,* January 1995; and M. Meyer and A. Murr, "Not My Health Care," *Newsweek,* January 1994.
2. J. Quinn, "Lawsuits New Weapon against Managed Care," *Rocky Mountain News,* July 1994.
3. D. Karp, "Avoiding Managed Care's Liability Risks," *Medical Economics,* April 1994; and P. Gerber, "Pointing the Finger: Who's Liable in Managed Care Settings?" *Physicians Management,* July 1995.
4. Karp, "Avoiding Managed Care's Liability Risks"; and H. Larkin, "Lurking Liabilities," *American Medical News,* June 1995.
5. Larkin, "Lurking Liabilities."
6. Karp, "Avoiding Managed Care's Liability Risks."
7. Larkin, "Lurking Liabilities."
8. Karp, "Avoiding Managed Care's Liability Risks."
9. Larkin, "Lurking Liabilities."
10. L. Kertesz, "Kaiser Ads: We're Not Like Other HMOs," and "Kaiser Physicians Unhappy with Changes, Memo Shows," *Modern Healthcare,* February 1996.
11. R. Lowes, "Dropping a Bad HMO Patient? Do It Very Carefully," *Medical Economics,* August 1995.
12. J. Smith, "HMO Reform," *LACMA Physician,* October 1994.
13. R. Ratcliff, "The New Wave in 'Managed Care' Laws," *Group Practice Managed Healthcare News,* September 1995.

10
CHAPTER

Summary

"It's difficult to remember that the job was originally to drain the swamp when you're up to your waist in alligators." I would bet almost everyone has heard that adage at one time or another. The tunnel vision that comes with fighting for survival is difficult to overcome. Capitated care is a new breed of alligator. I watch the panic of colleagues as they attempt to be included in capitated care. They sign contracts first and try to make it work later. Almost every administrator in California is proud to announce how many capitated lives the facility has contracted to cover. Yet, it is ironic that the major purpose of signing capitated contracts and bringing in new business is not growth, it's survival.

So backing away from alligators, we must focus on the swamp we set out to drain—that is, our original job was to provide healthcare. From its inception, insurance was primarily a scheme to supplement wages, and secondarily to provide healthcare coverage. As physicians accepted assignment of benefits and waited for reimbursement, insurance became a basis of credit.

As more insurance companies entered the market and competed for premium dollars, profit margins decreased. Combined with increased use of costly technology and a longer living population, financial demands on insurance companies threatened their survival. In response, insurance companies adopted strategies to retain as much profit as possible. This, of course, meant paying as little as possible in benefits. As these strategies failed to outpace rising medical costs, newer models of healthcare delivery were developed. Newest on the scene is fully capitated coverage, otherwise known as at-risk policies.

It is my opinion that these at-risk policies threaten the survival of the medical industry. The reason is the actuarial data on which utilization is based do not allow for accurate prediction. However, if properly collected, the in-office data can allow for greater accuracy in prediction of use, outcomes, and costs.

The ability to collect accurate in-office data is paramount in importance for providers participating in managed care and fully capitated environments. Physicians and other healthcare providers need to develop new ways of doing business, such as using more effective and accurate data and accounting systems, and to adopt new ways of looking at the business of healthcare.

The following statements reflect my philosophy of the business of medicine. I offer them as a new template for doing business.

- Patients are always the most important aspect of healthcare and shouldn't be lost in the machinery.
- Managed care evolved naturally in an insurance industry facing diminishing profits.
- Physicians should view insurance plans from the basis of credit.
- The data from insurance companies are inaccurate.
- Insurance companies are in competition with physicians for profit.
- Physicians have been blamed for rising medical costs, but all parties involved have some responsibility.
- The diagnosis is the driver of the data.
- The data collected cannot accurately predict utilization.
- As risk is shifted to physicians, they must fully understand the variances between their in-office data and insurance carrier data.
- Healthcare providers can generate data superior to current insurance company actuarial data.
- Providers must also update support systems such as accounting to maintain and improve profitability.
- Insurance carriers are avoiding the issue of bad data and shifting risk to physicians.
- Physicians and providers need to climb out of the swamp and reevaluate the situation, retool their approach, and regain control, rather than allow the alligators, the insurance carriers, to be in control.

INDEX